TEMPLAR CHRONICLES
WORLD COMPANION

JOSEPH NASSISE

HARBINGER BOOKS

ABOUT THIS BOOK

I began writing what would eventually become Heretic, the first book in the Templar Chronicles series, back in 2003, after selling the novel based on just the general concept as part of a two-book deal to Amy Pierpont, Executive Editor at Simon & Schuster.

Over the last sixteen years, that simple concept has grown to encompass eight novels, four novellas, and a number of short stories that have been published in six different languages worldwide, never mind audiobook and comic adaptations. I'm proud of the work I've produced and wanted to find a way for fans of the series to more information about the characters, creatures, and locations in the series right at their fingertips.

This book is the solution to that problem.

Think of it as an encyclopedia of sorts, a tome full of Templar goodness if you will, that can be used as a reference to the series as a whole. As time goes on and more books in the Chronicles are produced, I'll come back and update this volume with the new information that's been added to the series, creating a living, breathing guide to the world of the Templars.

All page references in this volume come from the second edition novels and novellas.

I hope you enjoy exploring the world of the Templar Chronicles as much as I've enjoyed creating it.

Thanks for the years of support and enjoy the ride to come!

Joe Nassise

PART I: THE TEMPLAR ENCYCLOPAEDIA

A SHORT HISTORY OF THE TEMPLAR ORDER

W elcome to the Jungle

Things are not as they seem.

That's one of the first things that a new initiate learns when being admitted to the Order. Things are not as they seem. We live in a world that frowns upon the existence of the supernatural, that values hard science over myth and legend, and that mocks anything that cannot be explained through scientific analysis and observation. The common belief is that anything outside of the easily explained cannot possibly exist.

The world is wrong.

Creatures straight out of myth and legend exist all around us. They move amongst us under the bright lights and in the dark alleys of our cities and they haunt the fields and deep woods of our rural areas.

Thousands of individuals come into personal contact with the supernatural each and every year. Many of them don't think twice about what they have experienced; they quickly bury the memory beneath swiftly devised rationale explanations, convincing themselves through sheer willpower alone that whatever they thought they'd seen or heard couldn't possibly be the truth. They convince themselves that their organized, scientific world has not suddenly taken a swift turn toward the unusual. Their encounters become nothing more than odd little stories to tell at office parties or over a beer at the local bar, something to be laughed at and ultimately ignored.

Others, however, annoy ignore it so easily. Unable to idly explain it all away, they devote their energies to learning more, to understanding what they have seen, heard, or experienced. In time, if they are lucky, they might be contacted by a recruitment officer and inducted into the one organization in the world that is devoted to protecting mankind from supernatural threats and enemies - the Holy Order of the Poor Knights of Christ of the Temple of Solomon, more commonly known as the Knights Templar.

Formation

History tells us that the Knights Templar were founded in 1119 by Hugh de Payens and eight of his companions in order to protect the pilgrims traveling from Europe to the Holy Land. They were recognized by the papal bull, Omne Datum Optimum, and given quarters on the Temple Mount in Jerusalem.

As usual, history is only telling us part of the story.

Yes, the Templars were founded to protect pilgrims traveling from Europe to the Holy Land, but protect them from whom? Or, more importantly, what? That's the part that history left out.

Hugh de Payens knew that the pilgrims journeying to the Holy Land were being preyed upon by all manner of supernatural creatures, from vampires and shapeshifters to demons determined to reap their souls. He petitioned the Church to be granted leave to destroy these beings in the name of Christ and was granted the right to create a military order designed to do just that.

So began the Templar Order.

―――――

BENEATH THE TEMPLE

One of the first things Payens did after taking possession of the quarters given to his fledgling order on the Temple Mount was to begin excavating the earth beneath their feet. Church legend had long suggested that Jewish treasures had been hidden there just prior to the destruction of the Second Temple by Rome in the first century and Payens was determined to prove those legends true.

To his amazement, he succeeded. In caverns deep beneath the Temple Mount, Payens found a number of powerful artifacts, including the Staff of Moses and the Ark of the Covenant. Perhaps even more important to the future of the Order, Payens discovered a veritable treasure trove of arcane information in the ancient scrolls stored with the Ark, one of which was a copy of the Copper Scroll later discovered in the Caves of Qumran on the Dead Sea. This scroll detailed the hiding places of a number of stockpiles, gold and other valuables hidden away before the Romans looted the city. Not one to look a gift horse in the mouth, and believing that this find was proof of the divine destiny of the Templar Order, Payen and his companions set out to retrieve as many of these treasure caches as they could.

―――――

GROWTH, Wealth, and Power

With the help of the ancient scroll, and the riches that it pinpointed, Payens and the Templars soon had a vast amount of wealth by which to fund their growing Order. Men, both influential and not, flocked to the Templar banner, wanting to be a part of what was soon a major military force on the continent.

With treasure to spare, Payens added international banking

to the Templar repertoire, inventing the modern version of banking. A noble could leave his valuables in a Templar facility in Europe, carry with him a letter of credit, and retrieve the same amount of treasure in the Holy Land, or elsewhere, once he arrived at his destination. This prevented the need to move large amounts of gold and silver across large distances, securing it against the marauders and brigands that sought to seize such prizes.

The Templars' prowess at securing valuables soon grew as great as their fame on the battlefield and it wasn't long before the major houses of Europe had entrusted their treasuries to the Order.

But their fame and extreme wealth soon cast a dark shadow upon the Order.

———

BLACK FRIDAY and the Diaspora that Followed

October 13, 1307. Black Friday. The day that changed everything for the Templar Order.

Jealous of the Templars' wealth and position in European society, King Philip IV of France began to plot against them. He secretly sent out a series of lurid documents in the early part of the fall of 1307, accusing the Templars of scandalous sexual rituals and the use of black magick, including the crimes of blasphemy and devil worship. Then, with the ire of the nobles firmly cemented behind him, beginning in the early morning hours of October 13, the King began to have the French Templars arrested and imprisoned for these offenses.

In the days and weeks that followed, more than 600 members of the Order, from Grandmaster Jaques de Molay down to ordinary workers who managed the Templars vast financial networks, were seized. Kept in isolation and fed meager rations, the Templars were forced under torture to give confessions confirming Philips's claims.

Horrified by the news coming out of France, and well aware that he'd been elected almost entirely through the patronage of King Philip, Pope Clement V issued a papal bull ordering all western kings to arrest any Templars living in their lands. That act sealed the fate of the Templar Order as it then existed. A few years later, in 1312, the Order was officially disbanded after the execution of fifty Templars, including the long suffering Grandmaster.

But the Templars had not been caught unawares. Word had reached the Grandmaster before the arrests began and the majority of knights escaped the coming persecution. The Templar fleet, long stationed at the port in La Rochelle, France, set sail two days before Black Friday. Eighteen galleons, loaded with the vast Templar treasury, escaped into the fog that morning, ensuring the Order would continue into the future. Molay, and the brave knights who remained at his side, did so in order that the forces of King Phillip did not grow suspicious and that their brethren might escape the coming persecution. The Rule of the Templars called for the brothers to defend one another and Molay's sacrifice set an example for the Order for centuries to come.

Pope Clement V eventually issued the Chinon Papal Bull that exonerated the Templars and restored their communion with the Church, but the damage had been done. The surviving Templars, now scattered to the four winds and vowing not to involve themselves in political affairs for the foreseeable future, remained in hiding, watching and waiting for nearly five hundred years.

———

Hitler and his Infernal Allies

Hitler's rise changed everything for the Templars. His alliance with certain powers from the Infernal Realms created a military force the likes of which the world had never seen and the atrocities the army committed during its conquest of Europe convinced the Templars that they had to once again to involve themselves in world affairs.

The Templars sent men to infiltrate the various Allied command structures, along with the newly formed Office of Strategic Services (the OSS). A large number of knights were therefore part of the advance missions into occupied territory prior to the D-Day landings and helped mitigate the impact of Hitler's supernatural allies against the US and British troops as they pushed inland from Normandy. (The spinoff series Templar Chronicles: World War will highlight some of these actions.)

Ultimately, the Order managed to influence events in a great enough fashion that the armies of the Allies defeated those of the Axis powers, saving much of the world from slavery at the hands of the Nazis and their brethren.

––––––––––

Restoration

Following Hitler's defeat, envoys from the Templar high command approached Pope Pius XII with an offer he couldn't refuse. Provide land from its vast holdings and financial support to get the initial network of facilities established and the Order would become the world's foremost defense against the Infernal races and other supernatural beings.

With the horrors unleashed by Hitler and his diabolical allies, the Pope didn't even hesitate. A Papal edict was drawn up, establishing the revived Templar Order as a secret combat arm of the Church, with the Pope as its titular head and the Grandmaster as its senior officer.

———

THE TEMPLAR MISSION

In short, the current mission of the Templar Order is to protect mankind from supernatural threats and enemies. The centuries in which the Templars refrained from acting as mankind's protectors allowed the return of supernatural races long thought vanquished and Hitler's alliance with the Infernal Realms, though ultimately defeated, allow evil to gain a major foothold in world affairs once more.

Today the world is full of dark and deadly things that look upon mankind as prey at best, playthings at worst, and the Order has its hands full on a daily basis doing what it can to mitigate the impact of such terrors.

———

THE RULE

As with the original incarnation of the Order, the modern Templars follow a code of conduct known as The Rule. This code contains twenty-three precepts that a knight of the Order is expected to follow, regardless of circumstances or provocation. These precepts, as laid out in the current Rule, include:

• Live to serve God and the Mother Church. Defend all that they hold dear.

• Destroy evil in all of its monstrous forms.

• Live one's life so that it is worthy of respect and honor.

• Live for freedom, justice, and all that is good.

• Never attack an unarmed foe.

- Never use a weapon on an opponent not equal to the attack.
- Never attack from behind or from hiding.
- Avoid deception and cheating.
- Avoid torture.
- Obey the law of king, country, and chivalry.
- Administer justice.
- Protect the innocent and avenge the wronged.
- Exhibit self control.
- Show respect to authority.
- Exhibit courage in word and deed.
- Defend the weak and innocent.
- Fight and die with honor and valor.
- Never abandon a friend, ally, or noble cause.
- Never betray a confidence or comrade.
- Respect life and freedom.
- Exhibit manners; be polite and attentive where appropriate.
- Be respectful of host, women, and honor.
- Loyalty to one's friends and those who lay their trust in thee.

CADE WILLIAMS, and the men of the Echo Team, have been known to break the Rule on more than one occasion. It is partially because of this that Williams has earned the nickname, the Heretic.

The Rule is first mentioned on page 13 of *The Heretic*.

TEMPLAR FACILITIES

As a worldwide organization that has been in existence for several hundred years, the Templar Order has numerous holdings in a wide variety of countries. Of these, the three most important types include the headquarters complex in Rosslyn Scotland, the various local commanderies on each of the seven continents, and the reliquary where the Order's mystical artifacts are stored.

Templar Commanderies

The air force has bases, the army has forts, and the Templars have commanderies. A commandery is the basic unit of organization within the Templar Order and is used to house troops in a specific geographical area. Each commandery is a self-sustaining operation, much like a modern military base, with access to almost everything the Order needs to maintain operations in that specific area for months at a time.

Areas with greater concentrations of supernatural activity have a higher number of commanderies. For instance, in the continental United States, there are a greater number of commanderies in the northeast, Pacific northwest, and along the California coast than in other parts of the country. This is most likely due to the higher population densities in those areas.

Commandery security is designed to maintain the Order's secrecy. High stone walls surround the entire property, regardless of location. Motion detectors, low-light cameras, and standard video monitors are mounted at strategic intervals along the periphery. Dogs and men patrol the grounds.

Entrances are controlled by cast iron gates built to withstand the impact of a speeding vehicle. Guards stand watch, dressed in the uniforms of a well-known security company, the company itself being one of the many businesses owned and operated by the Order without the public's knowledge. The guards themselves are both members of the Order and actual employees of the security company. The false identities they use for employment purposes can withstand a fair degree of scrutiny should the need arise (though their salaries go back into the Order's coffers through the credit union on which the checks are drawn).

Not all Templar security is aimed at the mundane, however. An elaborate series of blessings and mystical wards also surround any Templar stronghold, protection against any of the Order's many supernatural foes. At least one member of the Arcana Mysterium is on duty during each watch, supplementing the more mundane security measures.

THE RELIQUARY

The Reliquary is just what its name implies, a storage facility dedicated to the preservation and security of the Order's relics. It is maintained and guarded by the Custodies Veritatis and, much like the warehouse glimpsed in the closing frame of the first

Indiana Jones film, is the resting place for some of the most powerful objects discovered by man.

The Reliquary is first mentioned on page 176 of *The Heretic*, when Cade Williams and Sean Duncan are made aware of its existence by Preceptor Joshua Michaels. Cade visits the Reliquary three more times in the course of the Templar Chronicles. The first is immediately after the Spear of Destiny is stolen by the Necromancer in *The Heretic*. The second is when he steals the Staff of Anubis from under the nose of Preceptor Johannson in *Judgment Day*. Last but not least, the third time is when he and Gabrielle are searching the ruins of the Ravensgate commandery in *Darkness Reigns*.

Rosslyn Castle (Templar HQ)

On a high promontory that pushes out into the River North Esk about half-a-mile southeast of the village of Lothian stands Rosslyn Caste, the home of the Templar Order. Begun as a round keep in the fourteenth century, and expanded in the fifteenth century and again later in the sixteenth, the castle was originally home to the family Sinclair for hundreds of years.

A small portion of the castle is open to the public and can even be rented for special events for a limited time frame from the Land Trust. The damaged nature of the rest of the structure keeps public interest to a minimum. But behind this simple facade lies one of the most elaborate operational complexes in the entire world.

The Order has carved a home for itself deep within the mountain roots beneath the castle. A multi-story structure larger than the Pentagon but existing entirely underground provides the Order with everything it needs to operate clandestinely in the world above.

TEMPLAR COMMAND HIERARCHY

Much like the Church from which it originates, the Templar Order is hierarchal in nature and governed from the top down. A single individual, the Grand Master, sits at the top of the pyramid and governs the entire Order. His word is considered law. Descending downward from the Grand Master are the trinity of cardinals, the seven preceptors and then the commanders of the various directorates, before reaching the men in the field

THE GRANDMASTER

The ultimate authority within the Order rests in the hands of the Grandmaster. He has complete control of the resources and members of the Order and his word is considered law by those pledged to the Templar cause.

The Grandmaster is chosen by the Pope, often on the advice of the triumvirate of cardinals, and serves for life.

———

THE SENESCHAL

Day-to-day operational logistics for the Order as a whole are handled by the Seneschal. He coordinates all world-wide activities, ensuring they meet the guidelines created by the Grandmaster. For the most part, the Seneschal relies heavily on the preceptors (see below) for information as they have first-hand knowledge of what is happening in each region, with the Seneschal only getting intimately involved for large scale operations that include more than one preceptorship.

THE TRIUMVIRATE of Cardinals

The Holy See has appointed a triumvirate of three cardinals to help guide and advise the Order in difficult situations. While the cardinals' advice is not binding, it is given considerable weight by the Grandmaster himself. This, in turn, causes the various preceptors throughout the world to ignore it at their own risk.

THE PRECEPTORS

There are seven preceptors – one on each continent with the exception of Antarctica and two in Europe. All of them are men; all of them are veterans of the Order. They have served on the front lines, have faced the Order's enemies in combat, and understand fully the dangers inherent in letting the darkness gain too much control over the light. Selected by the Grand Master himself, the Preceptors serve at his pleasure but once instated can only be replaced by joint agreement of the Grand Master, the Seneschal, and the Trinity of Cardinals.

Within his region, the Preceptor's word is law. All decisions regarding how the Order will address or react to external threats and situations are in the hands of the Preceptor. Issues that affect more than one region are discussed among the preceptors jointly, with the Seneschal holding the final deciding vote.

TEMPLAR DIRECTORATES

The Templar Order is divided into six major directorates, each with a specific specialization for organizational purposes. These directorates include Operations, Intelligence, Personnel, Weapons and Supply, Science and Technology, and the Arcana Mysterium.

DIRECTORATE OF OPERATIONS

The Directorate of Operations is just what its name implies - the division within the Order that is in charge of running things day to day. Without it, the fight against the supernatural would have devolved into unorganized chaos decades, if not centuries, ago.

Information is gathered at the commandery level by agents in the field. That information is sorted, analyzed, and recommendations for action are then sent back to senior Operations officials at the headquarters in Scotland.

———

DIRECTORATE OF INTELLIGENCE

Information, particularly about supernatural threats and enemies, is at a premium and no one knows that better than the members of the Directorate of Intelligence. Tasked with discovering any and all information that might help in the war against the supernatural, the men and women of the DOI take their jobs extremely seriously because they know the lives of the soldiers in the field might very well rest on what they might be able to uncover about their foes.

———

DIRECTORATE OF PERSONNEL

Any organization of the size and scope of the Templar Order is going to need a team of individuals dedicated to know the experience and skills of its people and where best to deploy them. That's the mission and role of the Directorate of Personnel (DOP) with the Order.

The DOP keeps track of every single individual within the Order and manages the bureaucracy that comes with such a large organization.

———

DIRECTORATE OF WEAPONS and Technology

From flechette rounds used to impale vampires to the infrared beacons Captain Riley used against the ghouls in Tooth and Claw, the weapons and equipment used by the knights in the field are all developed, tested, and manufactured by the Directorate of Weapons and Technology, or DWT.

———

DIRECTORATE OF SCIENCE and Technology

Why does the moon cause shapeshifters to change form? What is it about ash wood that makes it such a useful weapon against vampires? What prevents the hordes of spectres existing in the Beyond from penetrating the Veil and invading our world? It is questions like these that are the responsibility of the Directorate of Science and Technology, or DST.

————

ARCANA MYSTERIUM

While faith is an important aspect to the daily operations of the Order, they would be remiss if they did not take advantage of the "holy" powers given to them by the Lord and it is for this reason that the directorate known as the Arcana Mysterium was created shortly after World War II.

The Arcana Mysterium, or AM for short, seeks to train those knights who show an affinity for magick and to use them as assets in the Templars war against the dark forces of the supernatural.

TEMPLAR SPECIAL UNITS

There are several special units within the Templar hierarchy that are tasked with performing very specific jobs that either require unique expertise or fall outside the typical chain of command. These units include the six elite strike teams, the investigation units, the protection detail, the relic hunters, the Custodies Veritatis, and the Templar underground.

STRIKE TEAMS

Seven elite teams operate within the Templar hierarchy; Alpha, Bravo, Charlie, Delta, Echo, Foxtrot, and Zulu. Each one is led by a senior officer, with authority over the teams as a whole falling to the Heretic himself, Knight Commander Cade Williams.

Each team consists of sixteen men, broken into squads of four men each. Each member is a volunteer and they must complete a rigorous qualification process. Only the best of the best make it into the unit, and when one considers that many of the men who join the Order in the first place have previous military/law enforcement experience, it is easy to see the stiffness of the competition.

Training is even more intense than the qualification process. Before being deployed, each strike team member is certified in dive operations, parachute operations, and demolitions. Teams can be deployed on twenty-four hour notice.

Much like the U.S. Navy's S.E.A.L. teams on which they are partially modeled, the strike teams have assigned sectors in which they normally operate. If operations require additional support, the team in the next closest local is activated first, unless other pressing engagements prevent otherwise.

Strike team assignments are as follows:

Southeast Asia – Alpha
Europe – Bravo
Southwest Asia – Charlie
Central and South America – Zulu
Australia and the South Pacific – Foxtrot
North America – Echo
Caribbean, Africa, and the Mediterranean – Delta

———

INVESTIGATION UNITS

Whenever the Order encounters anything unusual or unfamiliar an investigation is launched. These inquiries are controlled and executed by the twenty-four investigative units that are based in Templar facilities around the globe. The units vary in size and composition, from just a few individuals to teams of two hundred or more, with the majority of their members having knowledge of multiple disciplines.

Information gleaned from an investigation is sent to the Operations Directorate, where it is analyzed and stored in the master database so that it might be used to help the Order better respond to threats in the future.

———

PROTECTION DETAIL

Much like the United States Secret Service, the Templar Protection Detail is tasked with the protection and safety of the Order's senior members, starting with the Preceptors and moving up through the hierarchy all the way to the Grand Master.

Knight Lieutenant Sean Duncan was head of Preceptor Joshua Michaels' protection detail before being transferred to the Echo Team at the request of Knight Commander Williams.

The protection details are first mentioned in the Templar Chronicles on page 11 of *The Heretic*.

———

RELIC HUNTERS

The relic hunters are a small group of adventurous individuals within the Order that are tasked with hunting down and acquiring artifacts, or relics, of power that surface in the modern world. This is necessary not only to keep the relics from falling into the wrong hands but also to protect mankind from the knowledge that the supernatural not only exists, but so much of it would prefer to feast on humanity rather than peacefully coexist with them.

Relic hunters tend to be solitary by nature and typically work alone. The forthcoming Templar Chronicles: Relic Hunters series will focus on one such individual.

———

CUSTODES VERITATIS

The Custodies Veritatis - or the Guardians of Truth - are a special unit of twenty-five knights tasked with protecting and defending the sacred relics of the Order. When they are first mentioned in the Templar Chronicles, on page III of *The Heretic*, they are led by Knight Commander Nigel Stone and report directly to Preceptor Joshua Michaels.

––––––

THE TEMPLAR Underground

While not a special unit per se, the Templar Underground is a network of retired members that can provide resources and safe harbor in the event of an emergency. Often, many of these men are serving as Catholic priests or missionaries, allowing them to stay connected to the Order through official means. Father Burns, who provides assistance to Echo Team in *The Heretic*, is one such individual.

There are obviously limits to what this network can provide and having battle-worn knights showing up in their homes and churches is not something they look forward to on a regular basis. Still, they are oath sworn to provide what help they can before sending the knights on their way. Most take this obligation very seriously, though they will not put themselves or their families in immediate danger in order to help a former colleague.

CHARACTERS

Nearly two hundred characters populate the dozen volumes that make up the Templar Chronicles series to date. From mystics to mercenaries, saints to sinners, they all have their unique place in the world that I've spent the last fifteen years creating and populating. Here is a list and short explanation of the most important of these characters

Abbot Neil Martin

Abbot Martin is the Benedictine monk who is in charge of the Abbey of St. Lucius. He is first mentioned on page 102 of *Infernal Games*, when Cade Williams visits the abbey in order to steal the Hand of St. Bernard.

────────

ABROMOLECH

Abromolech is a demon that makes his home in the warrens beneath the city of Moscow. He is mentioned on page 212 of

Judgment Day as possessing two of the weapons known as Gabriel's Tears.

––––––

AGENT ROBERT WILSON

Agent Robert Wilson, Department of Homeland Security, is an alias Riley uses when it is necessary to appear in an official capacity while keeping the existence of the Order a secret. It is first used on page 44 of *Infernal Games*.

––––––

Andrew Kepler

Kepler is a crime scene tech from one of the Templar investigative units who Captain Riley enlists to track the SUV stolen by Cade Williams. Kepler is first mentioned on page 87 of *Infernal Games*.

––––––

ANNA RODRIGUEZ

Anna Rodriguez is a former Marine who is left permanently brain damaged in the wake of a terrible motorcycle accident. She is kept alive only through the assistance of machines and isn't expected to awaken when Gabrielle Williams' soul is transferred into Anna's empty body.

Anna is first mentioned on page 264 of *Judgment Day*.

––––––

ARAQIEL

First mentioned on page 173 of Judgment Day, Araqiel is one of the seven angels in the Adversary's former scream.

───────

ASHERAEL

Asherael is the true name of the fallen angel that the Templars know as the Adversary. He makes his first appearance in the Templar Chronicles in his guise as the Dorchester Demon/Slasher on page of *The Heretic* but is first mentioned by name on page 227 of *A Scream of Angels*.

───────

BARAQUEL

Baraquel is the name of the fallen angel that the scientists of the Eden Project restore to life through advanced cloning techniques during the events of *A Scream of Angels*. He is first mentioned by name on page 220.

───────

Benjamin (no last name)

Benjamin is the personal aide to the Lord Regent. He is first mentioned on page 153 of *Darkness Reigns*.

───────

BLONDIE

Blondie is a nickname given to former Templar Jonathan Bishop by Detective Joseph Burke on page 72 of *A Tear in the Sky*.

───────

CAPTAIN RED EYES

Captain Red Eyes is the captain of the ghost ship, Black Rose. He is first mentioned on page 178 of *A Tear in the Sky*. He is described as being at least seven feet tall with the girth to match and eyes of blazing red. He is dressed in high-waisted pants, a ruffled shirt, and sailor's boots.

CARDINAL CARLOS BOLLINGER

Cardinal Bollinger doesn't exist; he's just a name Cade Williams makes up as part of his disguise as Monsignor Evans when he visits the Abbey of St. Lucius in order to steal the Hand of St. Bernard.

Bollinger is first mentioned on page 102 of *Infernal Games*.

CARDINAL PAOLO GIOVANNI

Cardinal Giovanni is one of the senior cardinals in the Order and the person Preceptor Michaels reports to in regard to the attack on Ravensgate Commandery. He is first mentioned in *The Heretic* on page 12.

CAPTAIN EPHRAM BLACK

Black is an officer in the Knights of the Red Fist and is called upon by the Regent to go undercover into the local Templar cell to try and assassinate Cade Williams.

Captain Black is first mentioned by name on page 212 of *Darkness Reigns*.

CHARON

Charon is the ferrymen that guides souls across the River Styx in Greek mythology and is first mentioned on page 158 of *The Heretic*.

COMMANDER HAL BECKETT

Commander Becket is a member of the Knights of the Iron Fist and has the unpleasant duty of informing the Regent that an Iron Fist patrol was ambushed and executed by Templars. He first appears on page 155 of *Darkness Reigns*.

THE COUNCIL of Nine

The Council of Nine is a cabal of sorcerers, led by the Necromancer Simon Logan. Their symbol is the Ouroboros, which references their belief that entropy eventually devours all things.

They are first mentioned in *The Heretic* on page 44 and play heavily in the events described in "Down Where the Darkness Dwells."

Debbie Harris

Debbie Harris is the mother of Henry Harris, a U.S. Army soldier who survived two tours in Iraq only to be permanently brain damaged in a wreck with a drunk driver. Debbie is present when the Adversary, in Gabrielle Williams' transformed body, steals her son from his hospital bed and flies off with him.

Debbie is first mentioned on page 34 of *Judgment Day*.

DENISE CLEARWATER

Denise Clearwater is a hedge witch who Cade Williams met on a mission in Long Island early in his career. She is described as a fit woman in her late twenties, with long brown hair and dressed casually in jeans, a sweatshirt, and hiking boots.

It is Clearwater who Williams turns to when he needs magical assistance that he doesn't dare bring to the Order, such as setting wards over the soulless body of his wife, Gabrielle, after he exhumes her from her grave.

Clearwater first appears in *A Tear in the Sky* on page 25. She is also a major character in the Jeremiah Hunt spin-off series.

DETECTIVE JOSEPH BURKE, BPD

Joe Burke is a detective in the Boston Police Department and a former colleague of Cade Williams when he makes his first appearance in the Templar Chronicles on page 56 of *A Tear in the Sky*. Cade notes that Burke worked in "bunko," or a squad that dealt with swindlers and confidence rackets, while Cade was working in Homicide.

Dr. Raul Vargas

A physician at the Centro Medico de Especialdades in Cuidad Juarez, Mexico, Vargas was in charge of Anna Rodriguez, a coma patient with extensive brain damage and no hope of recovery. When the soul of Gabrielle Williams occupies

Rodriguez's body and she "wakes up," Vargas calls Special Agent Robertson and offers to turn her over to him.

Unfortunately for Vargas, Inquisitor Melvin Daniels - now possessed by a servitor demon - arrives first and Vargas does not survive the encounter.

Vargas is first mentioned on page 82 of *Fall of Night*.

DOCTOR MAXWELL WYATT

Dr. Wyatt is a Templar physician and the senior medical officer in the Moria Commandery.

He is first mentioned on page 219 of *Darkness Reigns* as the individual who treats Cade Williams after he has been poisoned by Captain Black.

DORCHESTER SLASHER

The Dorchester Slasher is the name given to the serial killer plaguing the neighborhoods of Dorchester, Roslindale, and Savin Hill during the final year that Cade Williams served as a Boston police detective. Also known as the Dorchester Demon.

The name is first used in *The Heretic* on page 65.

Dr. Burt Gardiner

Dr. Gardiner is the physician treating Henry Harris and the one who relays the bad news about the damage to Henry's brain to his mother, Debbie, on page 34 of *Judgment Day*.

Dr. Manoj Bhanjee

Dr. Manoj Bhanjee was the lead geneticist at the Eden Facility and in that role was in charge of the project designed to create a clone from the fossilized skeleton of the angel discovered by Father Juan Vargas years before. Bhanjee is ultimately killed by his own creation.

Dr. Bhanjee is first mentioned by name on page 150 of *A Scream of Angels*.

———

FATHER CAROL MOYNIHAN

Father Moynihan is a Templar priest and mystic who is called upon by Major Hale to confirm Cade and Gabrielle Williams' identities when they are first brought to the Moria Commandery.

He is first mentioned on page 150 of *Darkness Reigns*.

———

FATHER DEAN O'MALLEY

Father O'Malley is a priest from St. Judes Catholic Church. He is first mentioned on page 55 of *A Tear in the Sky*.

———

FATHER JAVIER GARCON

Father Garcon is a Templar priest that Cade Williams calls upon to assist with the interrogation the revenant that used to be Knight Corporal George Winston, believing the formerly devote man might take some comfort in Garcon's presence. Garcon is disgusted by the very idea and is just short of subordinate, but goes along with Williams nonetheless.

Garcon is described as a heavyset, balding man and first appears in *The Heretic* on page 98.

———

FATHER FRANK GIESLER

Father Giesler is the senior priest at the church in Durbandorf, Germany. Ultimately falling victim to the demons that invade the village, it is Giesler that sends word to the Templars at the Nurnberg Commandery asking for help. He is first mentioned on page 37 of *The Hungry Dark*.

———

FATHER JEROME NILS

Father Nils is the junior priest at the church in Durbandorf, Germany. He and two of his parishioners use makeshift flamethrowers to save Cade Williams and the men of the Echo Team from a demon attack on page 35 of *The Hungry Dark*.

———

FATHER PHILIP SMITH

Father Smith is a priest from St. Judes Catholic Church. He is first mentioned on page 55 of *A Tear in the Sky*.

———

FATHER JUAN VARGAS

Father Juan Vargas is a Jesuit priest and archeologist who for years was at the forefront of Biblical archeology. His triumphs include discovering the home of Pontius Pilate outside Jerusalem to excavating the tunnels beneath the fortress

Masada. He had quite a few failures as well, searching for the Ark of the Covenant, the grail chalice, Noah's ark, etc.

Three years before the events in *A Scream of Angels*, Vargas disappeared in the dead of night from a failed dig on the shore of the Dead Sea. Or, at least, what was assumed to be a failed dig. In *A Scream of Angels* we learn that the dig wasn't a failure at all and that Vargas disappeared with the most important artifact recovered from that site - the fossilized body of an angel.

In the wake of that discovery, Vargas used his connections and experience to finance the Eden Project, which eventually drove him mad.

He is first mentioned by name on page 42 of *A Scream of Angels*.

————

FATHER (AND MONSIGNOR) Michael Evans

Father Michael Evans and Monsignor Michael Evans are two aliases that Cade Williams uses during the events of *Infernal Games* and first mentioned on page 97.

————

FATHER THOMAS MARTIN, Society of Jesus

Father Thomas Martin is the Jesuit priest in charge of St. Margaret's Church in Broward Township, Ohio. Due to a previous position in the Church, he is aware of the existence of the Templar Order and is in a position to call them in when a revenant wanders into his sanctuary. He first appears in *The Heretic* on page 87.

————

Gabrielle Williams

Gabrielle Williams is the wife of Cade Williams. She was believed dead at the hands of the Dorchester Slasher/Demon for many years, until Cade exhumes her body and discovers that it is in a kind of suspended stasis. The hedge witch, Denise Clearwater, informs him in *A Tear in the Sky* that the body is empty and that her soul is "elsewhere."

Later in the series, the Necromancer Simon Logan steals Gabrielle's body and uses it in a ritual designed to bring the Adversary back to the material world. In doing so, he restores Gabrielle's soul, but also locks the essence of the Adversary inside her body as well, where the two begin fighting for control.

It is only Cade's actions in an attempt to destroy the Adversary with one of Gabriel's Tears in *Judgment Day* that Gabbi's soul is set free and inhabits the empty body of Anna Rodriguez.

During the first three books in the series, Gabrielle occasionally breaks the confines of her imprisonment and crosses the Beyond to appear to Cade in the real world. When she does, she is described as a beautiful woman, with a dancer's body and long auburn hair but with half of her face stripped of its flesh, showing the muscle and tendons beneath. She usually appears in a long, hooded robe, like the Ferryman that governs the passage across the River Styx, hiding what she has become. If her face is exposed, it will waver between the two extremes, like a poorly cast illusion, each version struggling to exert itself over the other.

Gerald Swanson

Gerald Swanson is an alias that is supplied for Cade Williams by Seneschal Ferguson on par 188 of *Judgment Day*, complete with a forged passport and driver's license.

———

Grandmaster Antoine Devereaux

Antoine Devereaux is Grandmaster of the Templar Order during the events of the first five books in the series. He is killed by the Adversary, who blames it on Cade Williams.

Devereaux is first mentioned on page 98 of *Judgment Day*.

———

Grandmaster Jacques de Molay

Jacques de Molay was the Grandmaster of the Templars when the King of France conspired with the Pope to persecute the Order. He was captured and imprisoned with a number of his knights on Black Friday, October 13, 1307, and eventually burned at the stake after falsely being convicted of heresy.

Molay is first mentioned in *Shades of Blood* on page 4.

———

GRANDMASTER NICO BRUNELLI

Brunelli is Grandmaster of the Order from 1971 through 1978. It is during his tenure that the decision to stop interfering in the actions of the Forsaken One is made, with all records of the creature removed from the computer archives, leaving only the written record of him in the Histories for posterity's sake.

Grandmaster Brunelli is mentioned for the first time in the Templar Chronicles on page 119 of *Judgment Day*.

———

Henry Harris

Henry is a U.S. Army soldier who survived two tours in Iraq

only to be permanently brain damaged in a wreck with a drunk driver. A steel rod punctured his skull, destroying the major centers of his brain, leaving him in a permanent vegetative state. Henry's body is stolen by the Adversary to serve as a vessel for one of the other members of his scream on page 34 of *Judgment Day*.

Ilyana Verikoff

Ilyana Verikoff is a succubus working as a dancer at The Blood Entrails who speaks briefly to Cade Williams on page 183 of *Darkness Reigns*. (Ilyana also made an appearance in *Watcher of the Dark* as one of Jeremiah Hunt's companions.)

INQUISITOR MELVIN DANIELS

Inquisitor Daniels serves as the prosecution during the court-martial of Knight Captain Matthew Riley during the events detailed in *Fall of Night* and appears for the first time on page 56 of that volume. Later, Daniels is killed by Seneschal Ferguson and his body possessed by a servitor demon, who uses it to pursue Gabrielle Williams.

INQUISITOR EDWARD HUGHES

Edward Hughes is a member of the Sacred Office for the Propagation of the Faith, once known as the Inquisition. It is Hughes who tortures Cade Williams, using Cade's power of psychometry to flood his mind with memories - violent memories - that aren't his own on page 161 of *Judgment Day*.

———

Jacob (no last name)

Jacob is an elderly farmer rescued from a patrol of Knights of the Iron Fist along with his daughter, Stephanie, by Cade and Gabrielle Williams. Jacob is the first person the Williams speak to after their return from the Beyond and it is he that informs them about the rise of the demons and the fall of civilization.

Jacob first appears on page 101 of *Darkness Reigns*.

———

Jake Caruso

Jake Caruso is a fake name used by Cade Williams on page 55 of *A Tear in the Sky*.

———

Jenny Olsen

Jenny Olsen is a young woman who is killed by a pack of ghouls in the opening scene of *Tooth and Claw*.

———

Jonathan Donaldson

Jonathan Donaldson is both the personal aide to Preceptor Joshua Michaels and a mole placed with the Templar Order by the Necromancer, Simon Logan. Donaldson is responsible for the death of Preceptor Michaels and allowing the Council of Nine access to the Reliquary in order to recover the Spear of Destiny.

Donaldson is first mentioned on page 171 of *The Heretic*.

JUAN ALVAREZ

Juan Alvarez is a Bridgeport, Connecticut drug dealer who appears in the opening chapter of *The Heretic*. (First identified by name on page 3.) Unknown to Alvarez, his body is inhabited by an unclassified demon, which tries to break free in the midst of questioning being conducted by Cade Williams. As a result, Cade is forced to put a bullet through the man's head, killing both Alvarez and the demon his body housed.

Kabaiel

Kabaiel is one of the seven angels in Asherael's scream that Fall with him and is first mentioned in *Judgment Day* on page 209.

KNIGHT CAPTAIN ORLANDO BAKER

Knight Captain Baker is the commander of Echo Team's 3rd Squad and is first mentioned on page 203 of *The Heretic*.

KNIGHT CAPTAIN DARYL COATES

Captain Coates is the officer in charge of the mission to attack a convoy of supply trucks headed for the Regent's headquarters on page 199 of *Darkness Reigns*.

KNIGHT CAPTAIN MIQUEL JUAREZ

Captain Juarez is the commander of Charlie Team. He is mentioned briefly on page 170 of *A Tear in the Sky*.

————

KNIGHT CAPTAIN CHARLES MASON

Captain Mason is a Templar commandeer in charge of the 3rd Platoon. He and his men are assigned the job of investigating the Eden facility, but fall back and request the help of Echo Team when they sustain heavy casualties during their initial inspection.

Mason briefs the Echo Team in his first appearance in the Templar Chronicles on page 42 of *A Scream of Angels*.

————

KNIGHT CAPTAIN NOEL STANTON

Knight Captain Stanton is the commander of the Folkenberg Commandery. He is described as a stocky man in his mid-forties with close-cropped dar hair when he is first encountered by Knight Commander Williams on page 85 of *The Heretic*.

————

KNIGHT CAPTAIN ISAIAH SULLIVAN

Captain Sullivan is temporary commander of Echo's 1st Squad during the incursion into the Beyond to investigate the Chiang Shih presence. He is first mentioned on page 177 of *A Tear in the Sky*.

————

KNIGHT COLONEL DAMIAN **Mombasa**

Colonel Mombasa is the short, dark-skinned commander of all mainline combat units stationed at Ravensgate Commandery. He first appears in the Templar Chronicles on page 62 of Fall of Night, where he is one of three judge at the court-martial of Knight Captain Riley.

Mombasa casts the one innocent vote, setting Riley free.

———

KNIGHT COMMANDER CADE WILLIAMS

Cade Williams is the hero of the Templar Chronicles series and the primary point-of-view character. He is a veteran of the Order when the story begins in *The Heretic* and a man torn between his thirst for vengeance and his duty to the Templars.

Cade is of average height but has an athletically muscular frame. His good eye is steel grey, his damaged one nothing but a milky orb. A web of scar tissue surrounds the eye, extending down his cheek, and he wears a black eye patch to cover most of the damage. Thin, flesh colored gloves cover his hands at all times, except when he is using his Gift. His hair is dark, shoulder-length, and stringy.

A former STOP (Special Tactics and Operations) team sniper with the Boston PD, Cade's life was irrevocably changed when he came face-to-face five years prior to the events of The Heretic with the supernatural entity known as the Adversary. His wife, Gabrielle, was killed and Cade acquired certain unusual abilities as a result of that encounter. Driven by a thirst for vengeance, he sought out and joined the Templar Order, rising quickly through its ranks to his present position, leading the Order's most elite combat unit, Echo Team.

———

KNIGHT COMMANDER MITCHEL GANT

Commander Gant is the current leader of Charlie Team during the events of *Fall of Night*. It is Gant who informs Captain Riley of the death of the Grandmaster, the subsequent seizure of control of the Order by Preceptor Johannson, and the fact that arrest warrants have been issued for all the strike team commanders, including Riley.

Gant first appears on page 194 of *Fall of Night*.

KNIGHT COMMANDER NIGEL Stone

Knight Commander Nigel Stone is a British knight and the leader of the Custodes Veritatis when he first makes an appearance in the Templar Chronicles on page 124 of *The Heretic*. He sets up a rendezvous with Cade Williams at a safe house in Otter Lake, but is attacked by the Council of Nine before the two have a chance to meet.

KNIGHT COMMANDER DAVID TYLER

Commander Tyler is the Beta Team leader when Preceptor Johannson seizes control of the Order. When Tyler resists arrest in the wake of Johannson's orders, he is gunned down by overzealous knights.

Tyler is first mentioned on page 194 of *Fall of Night*.

Knight Commander Silas Green

Commander Green was the leader of Gamma Team until he was corrupted with a conqueror worm by the Adversary in his guise as Seneschal Ferguson and forced to do his bidding. Green is later ordered to assassinate Gabrielle Williams, an attempt which fails thanks to the archangel Uriel.

Green is first introduced on page 180 of *Fall of Night*.

―――――

KNIGHT CORPORAL STEVEN Cerce

First appearing on page 144 of *Fall of Night*, Corporal Cerce is one of the eight men Captain Riley takes with him to Dalton's Ridge to arrest the shapeshifter Leroy Wilson.

―――――

KNIGHT CORPORAL LEON DALTON

Corporal Dalton is a crony of Preceptor Johannson, one of the new men in the ranks, who threatens Cade Williams while he is being transported as a prisoner to Ravensgate. Williams knocks Dalton unconscious when the guard gets too close and then blames the injury on the fact the man wasn't wearing a seatbelt.

Dalton is first mentioned on page 67 of *Judgment Day*.

―――――

KNIGHT CORPORAL OLIVER Dent

Corporal Dent is a member of Preceptor Johannson's protection detail and first mentioned on page 124 of *Judgment Day*.

―――――

KNIGHT CORPORAL DANIEL HARGRAVES

Corporal Hargraves is a Templar knight injured in the confrontation with the croatan on page 42 of *Fall of Night*.

————

KNIGHT CORPORAL JONAS HELMS

Corporal Helms is a member of the strike team led by Gabrielle Williams against Work Camp 352. Helms remains behind after the attack is discovered by the Regent's troops in order to pick the locks on the cages of the female prisoners. When he and Gabrielle Williams are captured by the Regent's forces, he is executed on the spot.

Helms first appears in the Templar Chronicles on page 229 of *Darkness Reigns*.

————

KNIGHT CORPORAL REGINALD JACKSON

Knight Corporal Jackson was a member of 3rd Platoon's D Squad. He was part of the advance team that entered the Eden facility after its discovery and was the only member to make it out alive. He died from his injuries shortly thereafter.

Jackson is first mentioned on page 48 of *A Scream of Angels*.

————

KNIGHT CORPORAL JAMES REESE

Reese is a former member of Bravo Team who was stationed at the Folkenberg commandery during the events of *The Heretic*. Knight Commander Williams requested Reese's presence to help identify the revenant that was once Knight Corporal George Winston.

Knight Corporal Reese appears for the first time on page 98 of *The Heretic*.

––––––––

Knight Corporal George Winston

George Winston is a former Templar knight resurrected as a revenant by the Necromancer. He provides the information Cade Williams needs to properly identify the Council of Nine as the group that is attacking Templar commanderies.

Winston appears for the first time in the Templar Chronicles on page 96 of *The Heretic*.

––––––––

Knight Corporal Steven Savile

Corporal Savile is a Templar knight chosen to accompany Knight Sergeant Dean and Knight Commander Cade Williams on their mission to infiltrate the demon-controlled city of Lesser York. He is first mentioned by name on page 172 of *Darkness Reigns*.

––––––––

Knight Corporal Wen Kurita

Knight Corporal Kurita is the commander of Bravo Team's 3rd squad and is first mentioned on page 203 of *The Heretic*.

––––––––

Knight Lieutenant Jason Kyle Bishop

Lieutenant Bishop is a former member of the Echo Team who gave his life in a fight with a pack of Chiang Shih several years before the events of *The Heretic*. Unknown to Cade and the other members of the Echo Team at the time, Bishop was turned and has spent the last few years rising through the ranks of the Chiang Shih as an officer under the command of Princess Akiko.

It is Bishop who developed the plan to invade the city of Boston, partially to take revenge on Commander Williams, who he considers a traitor for abandoning him to their foes.

Bishop is first mentioned in *Shades of Blood*.

KNIGHT LIEUTENANT SEAN DUNCAN

A member of the Preceptor's protection detail who is abruptly assigned to the Echo Team, Knight Lieutenant Sean Duncan has the age-old power to heal with the touch of his hands. He believes his ability to be a temptation from the enemy and will refrain from using it except in the direst of circumstances. A strong believer in the divinity of Man and the power of faith, Duncan will be sorely tested by his association with Cade and the other members of his unit as they push the boundaries of what Duncan sees as acceptable behavior.

Duncan is the youngest member of the team. Like the others, he is in good shape, with blond hair and the fire of true belief in his deep blue eyes. Unlike the other three team members, he is left-handed. When Duncan needs something beyond his standard issue pistol, he will typically opt for an MK17 SCAR-H assault rifle.

Sean Duncan first appears in *The Heretic* on page 9. Like his teammate Malone, he will give his life in service of the Order at the end of *A Tear in the Sky*.

KNIGHT LIEUTENANT NATHAN JESSUP

Knight Lieutenant Jessup is on duty at the front gate of the Templeton Commandery when the Necromancer and his infernal allies assault the complex, as noted on page 39 of *The Heretic*. Jessup is killed at the very start of the battle.

KNIGHT LIEUTENANT SAMANTHA LOPEZ

Lieutenant Lopez is a member of the Templar strike team led by Gabrielle Williams against Work Camp 352. During the assault, Lopez is in charge of freeing the male prisoners and is first mentioned on page 228 of *Darkness Reigns*.

KNIGHT LIEUTENANT JIMMY MARTINEZ

Knight Lieutenant Martinez is the commander of Echo Team's 1st Squad and is first mentioned on page 203 of *The Heretic*.

KNIGHT LIEUTENANT WILLIAM Mace

Knight Lieutenant Mace is the commander of Bravo Team's 2nd Squad and is first mentioned on page 203 of *The Heretic*.

KNIGHT LIEUTENANT LUCIEN "MORO" Morohunmubo

Lieutenant Morohunmubo, or Moro, as he is more commonly called, is a Yoruba Nigerian who recently transferred to Echo after clashes with Vatican officers who didn't care for his adherence to the cultural religious traditions of his people. Always happy to take on seasoned vets with a streak of insubordination, Cade Williams brought him into the Echo Team where he has since proven himself in combat with the supernatural. His additional insight into things not necessarily Christian have also come in handy.

Moro is first introduced on page 18 of *Tooth and Claw* during the mission against the ghouls inhabiting Gales Ferry.

Knight Lieutenant Warren Stoddard

Lieutenant Stoddard was the commander of 3rd Platoon's D Squad when it entered the Eden Facility at the orders of Captain Charles Mason. Initially reported as missing, Stoddard's body, along with those of the rest of his squad mates, were discovered by the Echo Team.

Stoddard is first mentioned on page 86 of *A Scream of Angels*.

Knight Lieutenant Thomas Wilson

Knight Lieutenant Wilson is the commander of Echo Team's 2nd Squad and is first mentioned on page 203 of *The Heretic*.

Knight Major Thomas Hale

Knight Major Hale is the commander of the Moria Commandery. He is first mentioned by name in the Templar Chronicles on page 142 of *Darkness Reigns*, when he introduces himself to the commandery's newest guests, Cade and Gabrielle Williams.

KNIGHT MASTER SERGEANT MATTHEW RILEY

Master Sergeant Riley is the executive officer of the Echo Team and Cade Williams' closest friend and right-hand man. He is also the team's weapons and demolitions expert. He has been a member of the Order for nearly two decades and gets promoted to the leadership of Echo Team after Cade's forced retirement following the war with the Chiang Shih.

Physically, Riley is described as tall, black, and imposing. His expression is usually grim and his muscular frame makes attackers think twice before engaging him in hand-to-hand combat. He has dark eyes and a shaved head.

Master Sergeant Riley (later Captain Riley) first appears in *Shades of Blood* on page 1.

KNIGHT PRIVATE JASON Polnich

Private Polnich was a 28 year old guard at the Longfort Containment Facility and was on duty the night a mechanical error allowed the Eretiku imprisoned there to escape confinement. Polnich survived the initial attack, but died of his injuries later that night.

Polnich is first mentioned on page 8 of *A Scream of Angels*.

KNIGHT PRIVATE JUSTIN Care

Private Care is a Templar knight chosen to accompany Knight Sergeant Michael Dean and Knight Commander Cade Williams on their mission to infiltrate the demon-controlled city of Lesser York. He is first mentioned by name on page 172 of *Darkness Reigns*.

———

KNIGHT PRIVATE MARCO CHEN

Knight Private Marco Chen is a member of Echo Team's 1st Squad. He is nearly killed by the resurrected angel Baraquel while investigating the Eden Facility in *A Scream of Angels*. He first appears on page 58.

———

KNIGHT PRIVATE SAM CHILDERS

Private Childers is a member of 1st Squad and one of the Templar knights that accompany Cade Williams across the Veil into the Beyond, an experience that disagrees with hm physically, as detailed on page 112 of *A Tear in the Sky*.

———

KNIGHT PRIVATE NATE CHRISTOFF

First appearing on page 144 of *Fall of Night*, Private Christoff is one of the eight men Captain Riley takes with him to Dalton's Ridge to arrest the shapeshifter Leroy Wilson. Like Private Kelly, Christoff is killed by Wilson's pack before the team can be evacuated.

———

KNIGHT PRIVATE PHIL DAVIS

Knight Private Phil Davis is a member of Echo Team's 1st Squad and is first mentioned on page 58 of *A Scream of Angels*.

Knight Private Joseph D'Angelo

Private D'Angelo is one of the men who accompany Cade Williams and Matthew Riley to the confrontation with the Adversary in Undercliff Sanatorium. He is first mentioned on page 240 of *Judgment Day*.

Knight Private Stan Gibson

Knight Private Stan Gibson is on guard duty with his partner, Knight Private Neil Jones, when the Necromancer and his allies invade the Templeton Commandery outside of Cincinnati, Ohio. The pair stumble upon the Necromancer as he is trying to raise the spirit of a dead Templar and are overwhelmed and killed by the spectres the Necromancer raises in the process, as noted on page 47 of *The Heretic*.

Knight Private Eric Johns

Private Johns is one of the eight men Captain Riley takes with him to Dalton's Ridge to arrest the shapeshifter Leroy Wilson. He first appears on page 144 of *Fall of Night*.

Knight Private Neil Jones

Knight Private Neil Jones is on guard duty with his partner, Knight Private Stan Gibson, when the Necromancer and his allies invade the Templeton Commandery outside of Cincinnati, Ohio. The pair stumble upon the Necromancer as he is trying to raise the spirit of a dead Templar and are overwhelmed and killed by the spectres the Necromancer raises in the process, as noted on page 47 of *The Heretic*.

———

KNIGHT PRIVATE JOHN KELLY

First appearing on page 144 of *Fall of Night*, Private Kelly is one of the eight men Captain Riley takes with him to Dalton's Ridge to arrest the shapeshifter Leroy Wilson. Kelly is killed by Wilson's pack before the team can be evacuated.

———

KNIGHT PRIVATE BILL Kirkland

Private Kirkland, along with Sergeant Malcolm Gore, are the first two men to encounter a survivor in the otherwise empty town of Gales Ferry. He is first mentioned on page 18 of *Tooth and Claw*.

———

Knight Private Tom Leveen

Private Leveen is a Templar knight chosen to accompany Knight Sergeant Michael Dean and Knight Commander Cade Williams on their mission to infiltrate the demon-controlled city of Lesser York. He is first mentioned by name on page 172 of *Darkness Reigns*.

———

KNIGHT PRIVATE CHRIS MARKHAM

First appearing on page 144 of *Fall of Night*, Private Markham is one of the eight men Captain Riley takes with him to Dalton's Ridge to arrest the shapeshifter Leroy Wilson.

———

KNIGHT PRIVATE FELIX Mills

Private Mills is one of the men who accompany Cade Williams and Matthew Riley to the confrontation with the Adversary in Undercliff Sanatorium. He is first mentioned on page 240 of *Judgment Day*.

———

KNIGHT PRIVATE JERRY O'CONNOR

Private O'Connor is one of the men who accompany Cade Williams and Matthew Riley to the confrontation with the Adversary in Undercliff Sanatorium. He is first mentioned on page 240 of *Judgment Day*.

———

KNIGHT PRIVATE STEVEN PASQUALE

Private Pasquale is one of Preceptor Johannson's handpicked men that gets placed on the Echo Team. On page 136 of *Judgment Day*, Pasquale suggests that Knight Commander Williams be hung as a traitor and a heretic.

———

KNIGHT PRIVATE JOE Callavecchio

Knight Private Joe Callavecchio is a member of Echo Team's 1st Squad and is first mentioned on page 9 of *A Scream of Angels*. He is noted as being a first-rate marksman, but that doesn't save him during an assault by several reaper demons while in the Eden Facility. Callavecchio gave his life in service to the Order, as have so many before him.

––––––

Knight Private Sam **Stover**

Private Stover is a Templar knight injured in the confrontation with the croatan on page 42 of *Fall of Night*.

––––––

Knight Private Joe **Tamarro**

First appearing on page 144 of *Fall of Night*, Private Tamarro is one of the eight men Captain Riley takes with him to Dalton's Ridge to arrest the shapeshifter Leroy Wilson.

––––––

Knight Private Allan Whitmore

Private Whitmore is a Templar knight captured and killed in the confrontation with the croatan on page 42 of *Fall of Night*.

––––––

Knight Sergeant Stefano Bautista

Sergeant Bautista was one of the eight men Captain Riley chose to accompany him on the mission to secure the shapeshifter Leroy Wilson. As the new sergeant in charge of 2nd Squad, Bautista performs well and earns Riley's respect during the disaster the mission becomes.

Bautista is first mentioned on page 138 of *Fall of Night*.

Knight Sergeant Stephen Bodine

Sergeant Bodine is one of the eight men Captain Riley takes with him to Dalton's Ridge to arrest the shapeshifter Leroy Wilson. Bodine is shot through the leg during the mission, but survives and is extracted with the others.

Sergeant Bodine first appears on page 144 of *Fall of Night*.

Knight Sergeant Malcolm Gore

Sergeant Gore, along with Private Bill Kirkland, are the first two men to encounter a survivor in the otherwise empty town of Gales Ferry. He is first mentioned on page 18 of *Tooth and Claw*.

Knight Sergeant Memphis Lyons

Knight Lieutenant Lyons is the commander of Echo Team's 4th squad and is first mentioned on page 203 of *The Heretic*. After being injured in the war with the Chiang Shih, Lyons becomes the Templar weapons master (*Infernal Games* page 156.)

Knight Sergeant Manny Ortega

Knight Sergeant Manny Ortega is a member of Echo Team's 1st Squad and is first mentioned on page 3 of *The Heretic*.

Knight Sergeant Michael "Rollins" Dean

Knight Sergeant Dean is the first Templar knight that Cade and Gabrielle Williams encounter after returning from the Beyond in *Darkness Reigns*, (page 141)

Knight Sergeant Miles **Denton**

Sergeant Denton is temporary commander of Echo's 3rd Squad during the incursion into the Beyond to investigate the Chiang Shih presence there. He is first mentioned on page 131 of *A Tear in the Sky*.

Knight Sergeant Nicholas Malone

A veteran member of the Echo Team, Knight Sergeant Nicholas Malone is in charge of computers and electronic surveillance/countermeasures. He's the prankster of the group, always trying to bait the others, particularly Riley. When Cade is too busy with operational duties, Olsen doubles as the unit's backup sniper.

Physically, Malone is the exact opposite of his longtime friend, Master Sergeant Riley. He is short and stout, with reddish-brown hair and a closely-cropped goatee. His weapon of choice is usually a Barrett Light .50 caliber sniper rifle. He also carries a selection of throwing knives in a custom sheath on his left arm.

Malone is first mentioned on page 25 of *The Heretic*. He gives his life while fighting the Chiang Shih to help the members of the Echo Team escape from the Beyond in *A Tear in the Sky*.

Knight Sergeant William Meikle

A grizzled veteran of the Order who survived the Fall, Knight Sergeant William Meikle is a Templar knight chosen to accompany Knight Sergeant Dean and Knight Commander Cade Williams on their mission to infiltrate the demon-controlled city of Lesser York. He is first mentioned by name on page 172 of *Darkness Reigns*.

Knight Sergeant Nicholas Olsen

This was the original name given to the character Nick Malone in the first edition of the Templar Chronicles. When it came time to release a revised, second edition, the name was changed so that it would sound so similar to that of the character Sean Duncan.

The character of Nick Olsen first appears in *The Heretic* on page 25.

Knight Sergeant Vincent Pantolano

Knight Sergeant Pantolano is the commander of Bravo Team's 4th squad and is first mentioned on page 203 of *The Heretic*.

Knight Sergeant Julius Spencer

A former Templar knight whose rest is disturbed when the Necromancer tries to resurrect him as a revenant, Knight Sergeant Julius Spencer meets Cade Williams in the Beyond and relays what he knows about Simon Logan's intentions.

Spencer is first mentioned on page 108 of *The Heretic*.

Knight Sergeant Louis Swanson

Knight Sergeant Swanson is the commander of Bravo Team's 1st Squad and is first mentioned on page 203 of *The Heretic*.

Knights of the Red Fist

The Knights of the Red Fist are the personal stormtroopers of the Lord Regent. Their ranks were originally filled from Templar knights corrupted by the Adversary's influence and later enhanced with men who chose to side with their demon overlords.

This group is first mentioned on page 108 of *Darkness Reigns*.

Lady in the Tower

The Lady in the Tower is the nickname given to the Adversary's prisoner - Gabrielle Williams - while she is locked in the tower on the Isle of Sorrows. It is first used in *A Tear in the Sky* on page 209.

Lenestiel

Lenestiel is an angel, one of the companions of the Forsaken One. He is also one of Cade Williams' ancestors and it is Lenestiel's blood that runs in Cade's veins. In an effort to defeat the Adversary, Lenestiel poses as a human for several years, taking on the identify of Seneschal Colin Ferguson.

––––––––

LENNY ABRAMS

Lenny Abrams is a medium Cade Williams calls upon to speak with the spirit of Knight Commander Nigel Stone, former commander of the Custodies Veritatis. He is first mentioned on page 158 of *Infernal Games*.

––––––––

LEROY WILSON

Leroy Wilson is a shapeshifting werewolf responsible for the death of several young women. Preceptor Johannson orders Captain Riley and several men from the Echo Team to capture and imprison Wilson for his crimes, knowing all the while that Wilson's entire pack is present at Wilson's cabin on Dalton's Ridge.

Leroy is first mentioned on page 136 of *Fall of Night*.

––––––––

LORD REGENT

The Lord Regent, Viceroy of New York, Conqueror of the Northern States and Grand Master of the Knights of the Iron Fist is the former Templar Preceptor, Willem Johannson. After the Fall, he was given control of the northeastern United States as thanks for his service by the Adversary.

He is first mentioned on page 91 in *Darkness Reigns*.

––––––––

Magda

The woman identified only as Magda in *Fall of Night* is Gabrielle Williams' physical therapist. She first appears on page 17.

————

Major Jacob Barnes

When he makes his first appearance in the Templar Chronicles on page 106 of *The Heretic*, Major Jacob Barnes is the acting commander of the Broadmoor Commandery, having been promoted to that position in the wake of the attack by the Necromancer and his allies.

————

Malcolm Heigler

Malcolm Heigler was the butcher of the village of Durbandorf before falling victim to the protean demons that invade that place. He is first mentioned on page 64 of *The Hungry Dark*.

————

Malevarius

Malevarius is the proprietor of the Irish Rose, a tavern in colonial Boston. The Rose burned down one night with Malevarius and his daughter, Penelope, inside. The pair perished in the blaze and ended up in the City of Bones (aka the City of Lost Souls) in the Beyond.

Malevarius meets Cade Williams for the first time on page 206 of *A Tear in the Sky*.

————

MICHAEL SIMPSON

Michael Simpson is a fake name used by Sean Duncan on page 55 of *A Tear in the Sky*.

———

MIGHTY BERTHA

Mighty Bertha is the name Stan Greenville gave his tractor trailer rig.

———

MIRACLE WOMAN of Juarez

The Miracle Woman of Juarez is a name given to Anna Rodriguez/Gabrielle Williams by the townsfolk of Cuidad Juarez when she wakes up from what had previously been believed to be a terminal brain injury.

The name is first used on page 21 of *Fall of Night*.

———

MITCHELL SLAUSEN

Mitchel Slausen is a neighbor of Jenny Olsen. Jenny attempts to enlist his help when she is being chased by ghouls, pounding on his door to no avail on page 4 of *Tooth and Claw*.

———

NIALL O'CONNOR

Niall O'Connor is a freelance operative who can sense the ebb and flow of magickal power. He is hired by the Necromancer to determine the authenticity of the artifacts in the Hofberg Treasure Palace and the Vatican Basilica that are claimed to be the true Spear of Destiny. Once he accomplishes his mission, O'Connor is killed by the Necromancer.

His first appearance is on page 6 of *The Heretic*.

————

Novitiate Parkins

Parkins is a novitiate at the Folkenberg Commandery who meets the Echo Team when they first arrive and brings them to meet Knight Captain Stanton. He is first mentioned on page 85 of *The Heretic*.

————

OFFICER FLOYD JACKSON, BPD

Floyd Jackson is a retired Boston police officer and Cade Williams' former partner. He was present when the Adversary, in the guise of the Dorchester Demon/Slasher invaded Cade's home and took his wife, Gabrielle, hostage.

As detailed in *The Heretic*, Officer Jackson took a bullet to the leg after exiting their vehicle and never made it inside for the confrontation with the Adversary. He recovered from his injury, spent another ten years on the force, and retired a few years before the events of *Darkness Reigns*.

————

PASTOR NICK DUNCAN

Pastor Nicholas Duncan was a traveling preacher and the father of Knight Lieutenant Sean Duncan. When Sean was a young boy, he was forced to heal the sick and injured during his father's revival shows.

Pastor Duncan is first mentioned on page 57 of *The Heretic* during the scene where Cade is reviewing Sean's personnel file.

———

PATROLMAN GREARSON

Grearson is a Boston patrol officer that Detective Burke deceives on page 72 of *A Tear in the Sky* in order to leave the Church of the Blessed Sorrow unprotected.

———

Penelope

Penelope is the daughter of Malevarius, who, like her father, perished in a fire in their tavern in colonial Boston. She resides in the City of Bones, where she meets Cade Williams and Matthew Riley when they save her from a trio of Dreadnoughts on page 192 of *A Tear in the Sky*.

———

Pope Pius XII

First mentioned on page 3 of *Shades of Blood*, Pope Pius XII was the pope who rescinded the excommunication of the Templar Order.

———

Preceptor Hugh Ochoba

Hugh Ochoba is the Preceptor of Europe and one of three men who stand as judges at Knight Captain Matthew Riley's court martial. He is first mentioned in *Fall of Night* on page 62 and is described as a silver-haired man with a permanent scowl.

Preceptor Joshua Michaels

Joshua Michaels is the Preceptor of the North American region for the Templar Order. When we first meet him on page ii of *The Heretic*, he has been in that position for several years and is viewed as a competent and straightforward officer with the best interests of the Order first and foremost in his thoughts. (Unlike his successor, that is.)

Michaels is betrayed by his aide, Jonathan Donaldson, and dies during the attack on the Ravensgate commandery, setting the stage for Willem Johannson to assume the preceptorship.

Preceptor Willem Johannson

Willem Johannson rises to the position of North American Preceptor upon the death of Joshua Michaels. He is described as being tall and thin, with arms that move restlessly when he is speaking. He has a regal attitude and a clear sense of self-importance that makes Master Sergeant Riley dislike him upon first contact.

Johannson eventually betrays the Order, siding with the Adversary and disrupting the Templars from within. He is responsible for the retirement and ultimate banishment of Cade Williams, eliminating one of the most powerful members of the opposition as the Adversary rises to power.

Johannson is first mentioned on page 41 of *A Scream of Angels*.

PRINCESS AKIKO

In her human guise, Princess Akiko is a tall, lithe, beautiful woman of Asian descent with porcelain skin and long dark hair the color of crow feathers. In her true form as a Chiang Shih princess, she is a ruthless killer that feasts on the life force of any human she can her hands on.

Akiko is determined to gain more territory, and therefore more power among the Chiang Shih, so she lets herself be persuaded to attempt to seize the city of Boston by attacking from within the Beyond.

The princess first appears in the Templar Chronicles on page 146 of *A Tear in the Sky*.

RAMSHEAD

Ramshead is a nickname given to a particular fomori inside The Blood Entrails by Cade Williams on page 185 of *Darkness Reigns*.

SECRETARY PAUL JAKES

Once a powerful Templar knight, Jakes lost both legs below the knee in combat with a summoned demon in the Australian outback and served for a short time as secretary to Preceptor Johannson before being reassigned. He is first mentioned on page 9 of *Tooth and Claw*.

SENESCHAL COLIN FERGUSON

Colin Ferguson becomes Seneschal of the Templar Order after the sudden death of Jacob MacIntyre. What the Templars do not know is that Ferguson is actually the angel Lenestiel and he uses his position to guide the Order, and Cade Williams in particular, into position to thwart the actions of his longtime enemy, Asherael.

Ferguson eventually falls victim to the Adversary's plot to have the fallen angels of Asherael's scream possess the bodies of Ferguson and his angelic allies.

Ferguson is first mentioned on page of .

———

Seneschal Jacob MacIntyre

MacIntyre is the Seneschal of the Order when the Templar Chronicles begins and, as such, Cade Williams' superior officer. MacIntyre dies of a heart attack shortly after the events of *A Tear in the Sky*, allowing Colin Ferguson to succeed him as Seneschal.

———

Sergeant Ernest Jessup

Sergeant Jessup is an injured US Army soldier who Cade Williams suspected might be a target for kidnapping by the Adversary. Cade put him under guarded watch in his hospital room near Baltimore, Maryland on page 228 of *Judgment Day*.

———

Sergeant Edward Mason

Sergeant Mason is a mortally-injured US Army soldier who Cade Williams suspected might be a target for kidnapping by the Adversary. Cade put him under guarded watch in his hospital room on page 228 of *Judgment Day*.

―――――

SIMON HAMILTON LOGAN

Simon Hamilton Logan, aka The Necromancer, is the leader of the Council of Nine and is the man responsible for releasing the spirit of the Adversary from his supernatural prison in "Down Where the Darkness Dwells."

Logan is first mentioned by name on page 42 of *The Heretic*.

―――――

SISTER MARGARET

Sister Margaret is a Catholic nun and a friend of Father O'Malley. She is first mentioned on page 56 of *A Tear in the Sky*.

―――――

SPECIAL AGENT ROBERTSON

Special Agent Robertson is a special agent with the Federal Bureau of Investigation with a secret interest in the supernatural. He first appears in the Templar Chronicles on page 82 of *Fall of Night*.

―――――

Stan Greenville

Stan Greenville is a long-haul trucker who helps Gabrielle Williams cross the border from Juarez into the United States. He first appears on page 114 of *Fall of Night*.

―――――

STEFAN BRAUN

One of the townsfolk holed up inside the church with the Echo Team in Durbandorf, Stefa Braun has been infected by a drone from the protean demon and hears voice in his head. When they tell him to let the other demons into the church in the middle of the night, he listens to them.

Braun is first mentioned on page 39 of *The Hungry Dark*.

STEPHANIE (no last name)

Stephanie is the teenage daughter of the farmer named Jacob who helps Cade and Gabrielle Williams after they return from the Beyond in *Darkness Reigns*. Stephanie gets herself into trouble with the commander of an Iron Fist patrol and has to be rescued by the Williams.

She is first mentioned on page 102 of *Darkness Reigns*.

TABITHA JACKSON

Tabitha Jackson is a neighbor of Jenny Olsen and is the voice on the 911 call listened to by the men of the Echo Team when they are called in to discover what happened in Gales Ferry. She is first mentioned by name on page 13 of *Tooth and Claw*.

Tech Sergeant Nicole McGreevy

Sergeant McGreevy is a member of the Science and Technology Directorate and a literal whiz with computers. She joined the Order after taking down the pack of vampires that slaughtered her family; her only weapons a zippo lighter and a can of hair spray. Captain Riley uses her talents to try and track former

Knight Commander Cade Williams in an effort to reach him before he is arrested by the Preceptors troops.

McGreevy first appears on page 151 of *Infernal Games*.

———

THE ADVERSARY

The Adversary is the name given to the fallen angel, Asharael, by Cade Williams after their encounter prior to the start of the Templar Chronicles series timeline. He is also referred to as The Other by the Necromancer, Simon Logan.

The Adversary is first mentioned in the Templar Chronicles on page 4 of *The Heretic*.

———

THE DARK ONE

The Dark One is the name the residents of the City of Bones gave to the Adversary. It is first used on page 209 of *A Tear in the Sky*.

———

The Forsaken One

The Forsaken One is a nickname given to the angel Uriel and first used on page 111 of *Judgment Day* when Cade Williams discovers information about him in Templar records.

According to those records, this being was first encountered by the Order in Venice in 1579 by Sir Malcom Trent, who noted that while he was observing a battle between "a heavenly angel and a spawn of the pit" he happened to glimpse a third individual, "covered with writhing markings that appeared like serpents of venom," observing the battle from the other side of the conflict. When he attempted to approach, the individual swiftly departed the scene.

The same creature showed itself to members of the Order at various times throughout the course of the next 400 years, usually during times of war of global turmoil. The records make it clear that the being, nicknamed the Forsaken One, never became directly involved in any of the events, regardless of how terrible they might be, but merely watched them unfold instead. It was theorized that its mission was to observe, but for who or what reason no one knew.

Several attempts were made to take the watcher captive, the most recent during a mission in Cambodia near the end of 1975. All attempts failed. Most of the time the watcher simply evaded capture, but the last attempt ended with all six Beta Team operatives killed, their heads removed and mailed back to Rosslyn Castle with a message in Latin that suggested that in the future the Knights mind their own business and keep to themselves.

Efforts to apprehend the Forsaken One were stopped by Grandmaster Brunelli after that point and its name stripped from the Templar databases.

———

THE Heretic

The Heretic is a nickname given to Cade Williams by certain Templar knights who are uncomfortable with the rumors that surround him; rumors suggesting that he uses dark magick and other methods outside the Rule to accomplish his goals. These rumors are, of course, true to some extent, given his Sight and his ability to walk the Mirror's Road into the Beyond.

The first use of the nickname appears on page 13 of *The Heretic*.

The Necromancer

The Necromancer is the nickname given to the leader of the cabal of sorcerers known as the Council of Nine, Simon Hamilton Logan. It is first used on page 42 of *The Heretic*.

The Other

The Other is the nickname that Simon Logan gives to the Adversary. The name is first used in the Templar Chronicles on page 45 of *The Heretic*.

The Preacher

The Preacher is a mysterious supernatural creature who is mentioned as possessing one of Gabriel's Tears on page 212 of *Judgment Day*. He also plays a major role in the Jeremiah Hunt spin-off series of books.

The Seven

The Seven is the collective name given to the demon leaders that take over the continents after the fall of civilization and are first mentioned on page 166 of *Darkness Reigns*. The Seven are also the original companions of the fallen angel, Ashareal, and the members of his scream before his fall.

THE WATCHER of the Ages

The Watcher of the Ages is another name given to the angel Uriel and is used for the first time on page 165 of *Darkness Reigns*.

TOM O'MALLEY, Boston PD

Tom 'O'Malley was Cade Williams' first drill instructor at the Boston Police Academy and is mentioned on page 1 of *Shades of Blood*.

URIEL (AKA the Forsaken One)

Uriel is one of seven archangels that serve the heavenly host. (The others are Michael, Gabriel, Raphael, Raquel, Remiel, and Saraquel.) He is known by several other names as well - the Watcher in the Dark, the Chronicler of the Ages, the savior of prophets, the keeper of the truth, the slayer of the chosen, and the Forsaken One. Tradition holds that it was Uriel that swept through the cities of Egypt, slaying the first born, and that he helped bury both Adam and Abel in paradise.

Uriel is described as having skin the color of burnt sienna, with dark hair and eyes and pleasing, symmetrical features. His skin is covered with living tattoos that move and change, showing the viewer their possible futures as well as the past, and on this back are the stumped remains of his once great wings.

Uriel is first mentioned on page 111 of *Judgment Day*.

CREATURES

People, that is, human beings, are not the only inhabitants of the pages of my stories. The Templars exist to protect mankind from supernatural threats and enemies and there are more than a handful of those encountered in the series. Here are a few dozen supernatural entities that act as either allies or enemies to Cade Williams and the men of the Echo Team...

Banshees

Banshee are female spirits whose wail portends the death of someone nearby. While they do not actively show up in the Templar Chronicles, they are mentioned by reference in relation to a demon's howl on page 134 of *The Heretic*.

———

BARROW WIGHTS

Wights are semi-corporeal wraith-like creatures that inhabit burial mounds and ancient grave sites. Some say they are the resurrected souls of those buried there, called forth to protect their earthly remains. The touch of a wight can drain the life force of a living creature and they are best avoided at all costs.

Master Sergeant Riley mentions encountering a wight early in his career on page 122 of *A Scream of Angels*.

––––––

Boggarts

Boggarts are a kind of semi-malevolent household spirit that frequently cause disruption through small acts of vandalism and mischief. They like to make things - particularly small, shiny objects - disappear and can cause food to rot and milk to go sour at the wave of a hand.

Some say that bogarts are the corrupted form of more helpful spirits like brownies and pixies, though this has not been confirmed by Templar scholars.

Boggarts are first mentioned in the Templar Chronicles on page 47 of *Judgment Day*.

––––––

CHIANG SHIH

Also known as the Demon People or the Gui Ren, the Chiang Shih are a type of vampire. Originating in China and quickly spreading across the Asian continent, the Chiang Shih have recently been making inroads in both Europe and North America, supported in part by a large contingent that call the Beyond their home.

Cade Williams first encountered the Chiang Shih while just a newly-promoted captain in the Order, an event described in the original Templar story, "This Cleansing Fire." (Note - this story was later retitled "Shades of Blood and Darkness" and then was shortened to just *Shades of Blood*, which is now the first book in the Templar Chronicles Missions series.) These enemies of the Order return to face off against Cade and the men of the Echo Team again in *A Tear in the Sky.*

CONQUEROR WORMS

Conqueror worms are psychic symbiots harvested from the shores of the Sea of Sorrows in the Beyond. They look more like centipedes than actual worms, with twenty-four legs, a chitinous shell, and a double set of pincers growing out of either side of their mouths.

When introduced to the nervous system of another creature, they allow a host with magical talent to control the victim's thoughts and actions, much like a puppeteer controls a puppet. They will burrow through the skin of its victim, attaching itself to the central nerve branch at the base of the skull, and will remain there until the victim dies as there is no known means to remove them.

Conqueror worms are first mentioned on page 183 of *Fall of Night*, when Seneschal Ferguson uses one to take control of Silas Green, the commander of Gamma Team.

CORPSE HOUNDS

Corpse hounds are the resurrected bodies of large dogs. Their skin hangs on rotting frames, their eyes burn with an unholy light, and they move with supernatural speed and dexterity.

Simon Logan calls a number of them forth to battle the

Templars during the final chapters of *The Heretic* and are first mentioned on page 219.

—————

Creeper Vines

Creeper vines are semi-sentient vines that live in the Beyond. They are attracted to the life force of the living. Their typical mode to attack is to surround and wrap themselves about their prey, much like a boa constrictor, and then squeeze the life out of them, slowing feeding on the bodies afterward.

Creeper vines are first encountered on page 93 of *A Tear in the Sky*.

—————

Croatans

Croatans are small, bipedal goblin-like creatures that Captain Matthew Riley describes as " a cross between a pissed-off velociraptor and Gollum from Lord of the Rings." They have scaly hides that offer some natural protection from injury and the dexterity of cave spiders, allowing them to scurry along the walls and even ceilings of the tunnels they call home. Croatan society is tribal in nature and, as a species, they are highly territorial.

Cunning and intelligent, Croatan war parties use primitive weapons - spears, swords, and bows - fashioned from scavenged materials. They are first mentioned on page 36 of *Fall of Night*.

—————

Demons

Demons are the residents of the Infernal Realms, commonly

known as Hell, and the avowed enemy of mankind. The Templars rank demons in five classes, from practically mindless creature acting on mere instinct to powerful beings with genius levels of intelligence and cunning.

Demons are mentioned throughout the Templar Chronicles, the most famous being the fallen angel, Asherael, also known as the Adversary.

DREADNOUGHTS

Dreadnoughts are the enforcers and voice of the establishment, be what it may, in the City of Bones. They are described as large, hulking brutes of men with blood red eyes and a network of scars across their arms and bare chests, as if they had been regularly whipped at some point in the past. They wear stylized metal masks across the lower half of their faces and long armored skirts that fall from their waists to the top of their steel boots. They are often armed with large, curved blades that resemble oversized scimitars.

Dreadnoughts first appear on page 193 of *A Tear in the Sky*.

ELIOUD

The Elioud are the descendants of the Nephilim that managed to survive the Great Flood. They are mentioned for the first time on page 217 of *Judgment Day*.

Eretiku

An Eretiku (from the Russian word for heretic) is a woman

who has sold her soul to the devil and returns after death to feed on the life force of the living. Her appearance is deceiving, for while she looks like an elderly woman wrapped in threadbare rags, she is actually incredibly fast and strong. Meeting the gaze of an eretiku also results in a wasting sickness that, as Cade Williams describes it, "makes Ebola look like a common cold."

An eretiku escapes confinement at the Longfort Containment Facility in the opening scenes of *A Scream of Angels* and is first mentioned on page 8 of the same volume.

––––––

The Ferrymen

Named after the Greek mythological figure Charon, the ferryman of the River Styx, the ferrymen of the Templar Chronicles first appear on page 158 of *The Heretic*. Little is known of this group other than that they will occasionally ferry the dead across the Sea of Lamentations and other "waterways" in the Beyond for a price.

Gabrielle Williams poses as a ferryman and saves her husband, Cade, and his companion, Knight Lieutenant Sean Duncan, when they are pinned against the shoreline of the Sea by a pack of marauding spectres.

––––––

Fomori

Named for a supernatural race in Irish mythology, the fomori are the result of interbreeding between humans and demons. They are also known as half-men or prior men. They are first mentioned on page 177 of *Darkness Reigns* and are described as foul creatures that tower over the human around them, with mottled grey skin and eyes with vertical pupils of greenish-white.

———

GHOSTS

Ghosts are the incorporeal spirits of the dead that are bound to this place of existence, either unable or unwilling to move on to the afterlife. They can be harmless, little more than half-seen apparitions, or full-blown poltergeists intent on harming the living. Some believe that spectres are ghosts that have gone insane.

———

GHOULS

Ghouls are humanoid, flesh-eating monsters created by arcane magicks and unleashed like a weaponized virus, with no manner of controlling them once they've been released. They tend to hunt in packs and can paralyze their prey with a simple touch, making them highly dangerous to any Templar that must confront them. Thankfully, their usual lack of intelligence makes up for their offensive weaponry.

That is, until Echo Team runs into ghouls that can not only think but plan ahead in *Tooth and Claw*.

———

Harpies

Harpies are flesh-eating creatures with the head and body of a woman and the wings and claws of a large bird. They are intelligent and hate humanity with a passion for driving them from the skies they once ruled as their own. They are first mentioned in *Fall of Night* on page 173 by Preceptor Johannson, when he explains an attack by a flock of harpies was the reason he recalled the helicopter that was supposed to remain on station above Dalton's Ridge to pick up Captain Riley and his men after they had secured the shapeshifter named Leroy Wilson.

––––––

Hell Sow

The Hell Sow is a massive sow-shaped demon called forth from the Infernal Realm by a sorcerer in the story "Pig Roast."

––––––

Hellspawn

Hellspawn is the name given by the Templars to anything that originates from the Infernal Realm.

––––––

Howler Demons

Howler demons are class three demons that are used for guard duty, perimeter security, and the like by mages willing to interact with such creatures. They are cunning and have a fair degree of intelligence, but dislike authority, making them difficult to control.

Howler demons look like oversized panthers with three legs on either side of their body and two heads instead of one. They have a long tail with a flattened end that they use for striking and clubbing prey, but their primary weapon is a piercing shriek which they use to paralyze their prey.

Cade and Gabrielle Williams encounter a howler demon beginning on page 32 of *Darkness Reigns*.

————

Incubus

Incubi (singular incubus) are the male version of succubi, demons that draw sustenance from the act of having sex with a human, often draining the human of their precious life force in the process. Incubi are employed as dancers in The Bloody Entrails on page 182 of *Darkness Reigns*.

————

Mirror Fiends

Mirror fiends are another name for reaper demons and appear in the short story, "The Mirror's Road."

————

Nephilim

The Nephilim are a race of beings created when angels mated with humans. The word nephilim means "giant" or "those who have fallen" and it is typically believed that the Bible is referring to nephilim in the line about there being "giants in the earth in those days."

Tradition has it that the majority of the nephilim were destroyed in the Great Flood, but some of their offspring - the Elioud - may have survived.

Uriel discusses the nephilim legend with Cade Williams on page 217 of *Judgment Day*.

————

Nightgaunts

Nightgaunts are denizens of the lower realms that can be

summoned with dark magick to act as servants in the physical world. They are humanoid shape and size, with large bat-like wings that extend from their backs, jagged claws on the ends of their fingers and toes, and faces completely devoid of any features. They use their forked tongues to test the air and detect their enemies, much like a snake.

Nightgaunts are first mentioned on page 223 of *Fall of Night*.

––––––––

Ouroboros

More a symbol than an actual creature, the Ouroboros is typically depicted as a skeletal snake that is eating its own tail. It often represents the cyclical power of the universe, particularly the idea that all things are renewed through entropy and decay.

The Council of Nine use an Ouroboros surrounding the number nine as the symbol of their cabal. Rings fashioned with this symbol are first mentioned in *The Heretic* on page 107.

––––––––

Pig Demons

Pig demons are a type of class two demon that are mentioned in the short story, "Pig Roast."

––––––––

Protean Demons

Protean demons - also known as chimeras, changelings, and flesh-twisters - are demons that have a central hive mind and semi-autonomous drones that they use to corrupt anyone they encounter and provide more power back to the central hive. The drone burrows inside the victim and attaches itself to the individual's brain stem before spreading along his or her spinal column and nervous system. Once in place, the victim becomes an extension of the demon, just like the drone. The two have effectively become one, transferring the power inherent in the victim's spirit to the demon. As it gains more victims, it gains more power and therefore becomes stronger. Wait long enough, let the demon gather enough power, and it can grow to the extent that it is virtually impossible to kill.

Protean demons first appear in *The Hungry Dark*.

––––––––

Reaper Demons

Known for their ferocity and identifiable by the scythe-like claws, reaper demons have a thick neck and muscular torso connected to an ovoid, spider-like body covered in a chitinous shell. Their six legs allow them to move swiftly and surely, including up walls and across ceilings.

Reaper demons have long, gaunt faces of winter grey, complete with an oversized mouth full of teeth and eyes of liquid green. Atop their heads are wriggling masses of hair that twist and turn as if they have a life of their own.

Cade Williams and the men of the Echo Team encounter a pack of reaper demons while investigating the Eden facility. They are mentioned for the first time on page 122 of *A Scream of Angels*.

––––––––

Revenants

Revenants are corpses reanimated through the use of dark magick; the souls of the dead forced back into the decomposing flesh and imbued with a taste for living flesh.

They are first described on page 49 of *The Heretic*, but not named for what they are until page 82.

Rock Trolls

Rock trolls are a race of subterranean dwelling humanoids that are both rare and highly territorial. They stand at an average eight feet in height and are several feet wide at the shoulders. Their skin is described as being brownish-grey in color with a jagged, rough surface that reminds the viewer of unpolished granite (hence their name). Black eyes and a mouth full of teeth the size of boar tusks complete the picture, making rock trolls both fearsome to look at and encounter.

Captain Matthew Riley encounters a rock troll on page 49 of *Fall of Night* and barely escapes with his life.

A Scream of Angels

A wake of buzzards. An unkindness of ravens. A murder of crows. It seems that we've developed quite a number of unusual names for groups of flighted beings, so it should come as no surprise that a group of angels is known as a scream. Many believe this is a result of the deep, primal fear that humans feel upon first encountering such a being, but whatever the reason, the name seems particularly apt and has been in use by the Templars for centuries.

A full scream consists of seven angels, seven being a holy number representing completeness and perfection in the Christian and Jewish faiths.

A Sneak of Demons

In contrast to a scream of angels (see previous entry) a group of demons is known as a sneak. The origins of this terminology have been lost in time but the Templars continue to use the term despite this. Unlike a scream of angels, which are seven in number, a sneak of demons consists of thirteen individuals in all.

A sneak of demons is first mentioned on page 248 of *Fall of Night*.

Servitor Demons

Amidst the hierarchy of the infernal, servitor demons exist on one of the lower rungs. They are typically used for grunt work by higher ranking infernals and will obey to a fault.

In order to impact the material world, they must possess a body, either living or dead. In their true form, they appear as a shadowy humanoid form with spikes all over the body jutting out in various directions.

They are first mentioned on page 79 of *Fall of Night*.

Shadow Demons

Shadow demons are fashioned with dark magick from the souls of humans who commit particularly vile acts while alive. Their bodies are twisted parodies of the beings they once were and they hunt in packs like wild dogs. Crafty and highly intelligent, these creatures are often used to hunt down elusive prey and will pursue their targets until either the target has been secured or the demons have been banished back to the Infernal Plane through the death of their metaphysical form.

Shadow demons are first mentioned on page 248 of *Fall of Night*.

———

Sky Sharks

Called forth with the power of the Spear of Destiny by the Necromancer from some distant plane of existence, the sky sharks first appear in *The Heretic* on page 228.

The sky sharks are described as being at least fifteen feet in length, shaped like manatees but with functional arms instead of fins. They have bulbous heads with human faces and gaping maws full of oversized teeth. When they are first seen by Duncan and Malone, they are writhing and rolling through the storm clouds that surround them, their eyes full of hatred when they spot the Templar helicopter occupying the sky nearby.

———

SPECTRES

The primary residents of the Beyond, spectres are the souls of humans that have been corrupted by greed, anger, and hate. Creatures of spirit and will, spectres are manifestations of pure evil and as a result are impervious to any weapons that are not connected emotionally to their wielder. A sword might harm them, depending on how the bearer views his or her weapon, but a firearm never will.

Spectres appear multiple times throughout the Templar Chronicles, particularly at the behest of the Necromancer, Simon Logan, who calls them from the other side to serve as his shock troops when he attacks the various Templar strongholds during his search for the Spear of Destiny.

They are first mentioned on page 48 of *The Heretic*.

―――――

SUCCUBUS DEMONS

Succubus demons feed on the life force of human beings, extracting it from their victims while in the midst of sexual activity. They hide behind an attractive facade, though close examination will often reveal physical characteristics that exemplify their true form, from claw-like fingernails to vestigial tails and wings.

Sex with a succubus demon is said to be both highly enjoyable and highly addictive, creating a compulsion for the victim to return again and again until they quite literally die of pleasure.

Cade Williams disrupts a succubus' feeding on page 21 of *Judgment Day*.

―――――

THE FALLEN

The Fallen is a name given by the Templars to angels who have been corrupted and "fallen" from heaven's grace to become demons.

LOCATIONS

The Templar Order is a worldwide organization, with activity taking place in myriad different locations across the globe. Include here are nearly sixty specific locales mentioned in the Templar Chronicles to date.

ABBEY OF ST. Lucius

The Abbey of St. Lucius is a Benedictine monastery high in the Pyrenees Mountains of France. It began as a convent in the 1500s, was abandoned for a number of years, and then purchased by the Benedictines just before the start of the French Revolution. It has been in their control ever since.

The abbey sits high on a promontory, like a castle guarding the entrance to a mountain pass. It is also the resting place of the Hand of St. Bernard of Clairvaux.

It is first mentioned, though not by name, on page 101 of *Infernal Games*.

———

ARCHIVUM SECRETUM VATICANUM

The Archivum Secretum Vaticanum or Secret Vatican Archives, is the central archive and repository of information in Vatican City. Created in 1612 by Pope Paul V, the archives hold not only the official acts, state papers, and correspondence of those who have held the position of Pope, but also a wide variety of documents accumulated over the last ten centuries that the Catholic Church believes too dangerous for the average individual to read or even be aware of.

In *Infernal Games*, Cade breaks into the Archives, searching for information on page 87.

———

ARLINGTON COMMANDERY

The Arlington Commandery is a Templar facility located just outside Arlington, Virginia and serves the greater Washington D.C. area.

———

AZACUALPA

Azacualpa is a small village in the jungle of Honduras that is mentioned in the short story, "Down Where the Darkness Dwells."

———

BENNINGTON CONTAINMENT FACILITY

The Bennington Containment Facility is a Templar maximum security detainment facility, similar to Longfort.

———

Birmingham Commandery

The Birmingham Commandery is a Templar facility located on the outskirts of Birmingham, Alabama and first mentioned on page 114 of *The Heretic*.

Black Rose

The Black Rose is a spectral galleon captained by Red Eyes, the ghost of a 17th century buccaneer. It is first mentioned on page 178 of *A Tear in the Sky*.

Bristol Commandery

The Bristol Commandery outside Bristol, Rhode Island is the largest Templar commandery in North America and the seat of power for the North American Preceptor. It is first mentioned in *The Heretic*.

Broadmoor Commandery

The Broadmoor Commandery is a Templar facility in upper state New York. It is the third commandery that the Necromancer attacks in his effort to find the Spear of Destiny's hiding place in *The Heretic* and is first mentioned on page 106.

Centro Medico de Especialdades

The Centro Medico de Especialdades is a hospital in Cuidad

Juarez, Mexico where Anna Rodriguez was being treated before the possession of her body by Gabrielle Williams.

The hospital is first mentioned on page 82 of *Fall of Night*.

CHAPEL of the Sacred Hand

A small chapel in the Abbey of Saint Lucius, the Chapel of the Sacred Hand is the resting place of the relic known as the Hand of St. Bernard of Clairvaux. It is first mentioned on page 103 of *Infernal Games*.

CHURCH of the Blessed Sorrow

The Church of the Blessed Sorrow is a Catholic Church in Boston that Father Thomas Martin called home. It is first mentioned on page 44 of *A Tear in the Sky*.

CITY OF BONES

The City of Bones is another name for the City of Lost Souls. It is a city of ghosts and other supernatural entities in the Beyond and first mentioned on page 181 of *A Tear in the Sky*. It is identified by name on page 208 of the same.

CITY OF DESPAIR

The City of Despair is a collection of ruins in the midst of the Isle of Sorrows. It is here that Gabrielle Williams is being held against her will by the Adversary, according to the angel

Baraquel, as he informs Cade on page 227 of *A Scream of Angels*.

———

COUNTY MORGUE ANNEX

The County Morgue Annex is a secondary morgue facility for the city of Boston that is housed in the basement of Mass General Hospital. It is first mentioned on page 62 of *A Tear in the Sky*. It is here that Father Martin's body is examined in the wake of his murder by Cade Williams.

———

COVINGTON

Covington is a small town in northwestern Connecticut, near the abandoned quarry that Cade had set up as a rendezvous point just before Preceptor Johannson seized control of the Templar Order.

Covington is first mentioned on page 45 of *Darkness Reigns*.

———

DALTON'S RIDGE

Dalton's Ridge is an area in the Allegheny Mountains of northern Pennsylvania where the shapeshifter Leroy Wilson has made his home. It is first mentioned on page 135 of *Fall of Night*.

———

DEACONESS HOSPITAL

The Deaconess is a hospital in Boston where Cade Williams recuperated after the attack on him and his wife by the Adversary in the guise of the Dorchester Slasher. It is first mentioned on page 60 of *A Tear in the Sky*.

––––––––

DURBANDORF

Durbandorf is a small village in the Black Forest region of Germany. It is here that the events of *The Hungry Dark* take place and Durbandorf is first mentioned on page 3 of that volume.

––––––––

EDEN FACILITY

The Eden Facility is the secret research station in the desert of New Mexico set up by Father Juan Vargas and his associates so that they might attempt to create a clone from the fossilized skeleton of an angel discovered along the shore of the Dead Sea.

The facility is first identified on page 102 of *A Scream of Angels*.

––––––––

FIVE STAR CAFE

The Five Star Cafe is a local business in Stonebridge, Connecticut. On page 12 of *Darkness Reigns*, a newspaper inside the cafe allows Cade and Gabrielle Williams to discover where they are after emerging from the Beyond.

––––––––

Folkenberg Commandery

The Folkenberg Commandery is located seventy-five miles

north of Cincinnati, Ohio and is under the command of Knight Captain Noel Stanton when the Echo Team arrives. Men from Folkenberg were the first to discover that the Templeton Commandery had been attacked and it is here that Cade and the Echo Team question the revenant that was once Knight Corporal George Winston.

Folkenberg is first mentioned in *The Heretic* on page 76.

––––––

Gales Ferry

Gales Ferry, New Hampshire, is the setting for *Tooth and Claw*, Templar Chronicles Missions #3. The population of this small town vanishes without a trace, prompting investigation by the Templars, who discover a nest of ghouls beneath the city streets.

––––––

HILLTOP NATIONAL PARK

Hilltop National Park is a wooded area in northern Connecticut. The quarry Cade Williams chose as a rendezvous point stands on the edge of the park.

The park is first mentioned on page 45 of *Darkness Reigns*.

––––––

HOUSATONIC RIVER

The Housatonic River is a wide river running through western Massachusetts and into southwestern Connecticut, ending at the waters of Long Island Sound.

It is on a bridge spanning the river that Cade Williams discovers his wife's spirit is still trapped inside her body despite the Adversary's control of her physical form, events detailed on page 50 of *Infernal Games*.

IRISH ROSE

The Irish Rose is a tavern from colonial Boston that appeared in the City of Bones after it burned down in the real world, taking the life of its proprietor and his daughter when it did so. It is first mentioned on page 207 of *A Tear in the Sky*.

ISLE OF SORROWS

The Isle of Sorrows is an island in the midst of the Sea of Lamentations and it is here that the Adversary has a home base of sorts. The island is first mentioned by Gabrielle Williams on page 214 of *A Scream of Angels*.

Lafayette Commandery

The Lafayette Commandery is a Templar facility just north of Lafayette, Louisiana. It is from this commandery that Knight Commander Williams and the men of the Echo Team, supported by those of Bravo Team, stage an assault on the ruined plantation that serves as the stronghold of the Council of Nine.

The commandery is first mentioned on page 203 of *The Heretic*.

LESSER YORK

Lesser York is the demon-controlled city that sprung up in the ruins of New Haven, Connecticut. It is first mentioned on page 155 of *Darkness Reigns* and is visited by Cade Williams and a team from the Moria Commandery so that they might gain information from an informant.

LONGFORT CONTAINMENT FACILITY

Longfort is one of the most secure prisons maintained by the Templars, housing some of the most dangerous criminals and creatures captured by the Order over their long history, including the Necromancer, Simon Logan.

It is first mentioned on page 5 of *A Scream of Angels*.

MARKHAM'S SLAUGHTERHOUSE

Markham's is a slaughterhouse on the outskirts of Boston and the site of Cade Williams' first battle with the Chiang Shih. It is here that Knight Lieutenant Bishop is killed and brought back as one of the enemy.

It is first mentioned in *Shades of Blood*.

MASSACHUSETTS GENERAL HOSPITAL

Commonly known as Mass General, this is one of the premier hospitals in the Boston area and houses the morgue annex in its basement. It is first mentioned on page 62 of *A Tear in the Sky*.

———

MAXINE'S

Maxines is a bar in Boston where Detective Burke meets with former Templar turned Chiang Shih Jonathan Bishop. It is first mentioned on page 71 of *A Tear in the Sky*.

———

MITNAL

Mitnal is the nine-level underworld of the Mayan cosmology. It is first mentioned in the short story, "Down Where the Darkness Dwells."

———

MORIA COMMANDERY

The Moria Commandery is a Templar facility housed in an abandoned Department of Public Works maintenance facility outside of what used to be New Haven, Connecticut. Cade and Gabrielle Williams are brought here after encountering a cell of Templars in the ruins of Ravensgate. It is first mentioned by name on page 159 of *Darkness Reigns*.

———

NÜRNBERG COMMANDERY

The Nurnberg Commandery is a Templar facility outside Nurnberg, Germany. The Echo Team is on site helping train new initiates when the events of *The Hungry Dark* take place.

It is mentioned for the first time in *The Hungry Dark* on page 22.

Otter Lake

Otter Lake is a small mountain community north of Utica in the Adirondack Mountains of upper state New York. It is also the location of the Custodies Veritatis safe house when Knight Commander Nigel Stone arranges a meeting with Cade Williams. (Unfortunately for Stone, the Council of Nine arrive before Williams.)

Otter Lake is first mentioned on page 139 of *The Heretic*.

Pitchfork County

Pitchfork is a county in Missouri with more than the usual amount of supernatural influence. It is home to the Night Marshall, Joe Hark, and is mentioned for the first time in the Templar Chronicles in the short story, "Pig Roast," written in conjunction with Sam Witt.

Poveglia

Poveglia is a former plague island in the Venice lagoon that is home to the archangel, Uriel. It is first mentioned on page 118 of *Judgment Day*.

Ravensgate Commandery

The Ravensgate Commandery is located in Westport, Connecticut and is the second largest commandery in the eastern United States at the point it is first mentioned in *The Heretic* on page 11.

It is home base for Knight Commander Cade Williams and the Echo Team and also houses the Reliquary in the tunnels deep beneath the facility.

———

Red Hook Container Terminal

The Red Hook Container Terminal is a maritime facility that services container ships and bulk cargo headed to New York, New Jersey, and north into New England. It has six active container cranes, two bulk-handling yards, and 500,000 feet of warehouse space.

It is here, in warehouse 486, that the Necromancer meets with Cade Williams on page 197 of *Infernal Games*.

———

River Styx

The River Styx is the mystical river in Greek mythology that winds its way through the underworld. It is first mentioned on page 158 of *The Heretic*.

———

Rocky Mountain Kingdom

The Rocky Mountain Kingdom is a stretch of demon-controlled territory in the Colorado Rockies. Two envoys to the Lord Regent from the Kingdom are mentioned on page 209 of *Darkness Reigns*.

———

Rosslyn Castle

Rosslyn Castle is a partially ruined castle near the village of Roslin, Scotland and the ancestral home of the Sinclair family. It is also the secret worldwide headquarters of the Knights Templar. (See Templar Facilities earlier in this volume.)

It is first mentioned on page 10 of *The Heretic*.

————

St. Judes

St. Judes is a Catholic church in the city of Boston. It is first mentioned on page 55 of *A Tear in the Sky*.

————

Santa Limas

Santa Limas is a town in New Mexico. It is just outside the city limits that Father Juan Vargas is found wandering the desert raving about the apocalypse.

The town is first mentioned on page 43 of *A Scream of Angels*.

————

Sea of Lamentations

A large body of water at the center of the Beyond, the Sea of Lamentations is poisonous to the living and its depths contain the souls of the dead that refuse to move on to the afterlife. It is first mentioned by Gabrielle Williams on page 214 of *A Scream of Angels*.

————

Seaside Diner

The Seaside Diner is a diner in Stamford, Connecticut where Cade Williams meet Captain Matthew Riley after Cade has been declared an enemy of the Order. The diner is first mentioned on page 39 of *Judgment Day*.

———

Smokey's House of Meat

Smokey's is a barbecue shack in Pitchfork County, Missouri where the men of the Echo Team meet with the Night Marshall for the first time.

It is first mentioned in the short story, "Pig Roast."

———

St. Margaret's Hospital

St. Margaret's is a private Catholic hospital in Albuquerque, New Mexico. It is here that Father Juan Vargas is taken after he is discovered wandering in the desert.

St. Margaret's is first mentioned on page 43 of *A Scream of Angels*.

———

Stonebridge

Stonebridge is a small town in northwestern Connecticut. Cade and Gabrielle Williams emerge from the Beyond here, unaware that five years have passed in the real world while they've been gone.

Stonebridge is first mentioned on page 12 of *Darkness Reigns*.

———

TEMPLETON COMMANDERY

Templeton Commandery is a Templar facility outside of Cincinnati, Ohio. It is the second location that Simon Logan, the Necromancer, attacks during his quest to obtain the Spear of Destiny.

Templeton Commandery is first mentioned on page 39 of *The Heretic*.

———

THE BEYOND

Just a whisper away from our own world, there lies another. A world of darkness and shadow, of pain and suffering. A world where the dead roam free and the living rarely intrude. It goes by many names in many cultures, but to the Templars, it's simply known as the Beyond.

The Beyond is a mirror image of our world, but based on a spiritual, rather than physical, reality.

A thin mystical barrier known as the Veil separates our world from the next. It serves to keep the majority of the Beyond's denizens from invading our reality. It is not foolproof, however. From time to time various entities will find the will or the means to cross the barrier and, depending upon their power, take up residence here.

Throughout the ages certain individuals have been able to pierce the Veil and make the journey in the other direction as well. Cade Williams is one of those individuals and, later in the Templar Chronicles, it is revealed that his wife, Gabrielle, is another.

The Beyond is first mentioned on page 73 of *The Heretic*.

———

THE BLOODY ENTRAILS

The Bloody Entrails is a bar/nightclub that stands in the back alleys of Lesser York and is used as a meeting place between the Templars and an informant in the employee of the demon contingent that rules the city.

The bar is first mentioned in the Templar Chronicles on page 175 of *Darkness Reigns*.

––––––

TONCONTIN INTERNATIONAL AIRPORT

Toncontin International Airport is a civil and military airport that serves Tegucigalpa, Honduras. It is considered one of the top ten most dangerous airports in the world and is first mentioned in the Templar Chronicles in the short story, "Down Where the Darkness Dwells."

––––––

UNDERCLIFF SANATORIUM

Originally opened in 1910 under the name Meriden Sanitorium, this facility had been expanded over the years and served a variety of purposes - from a mental hospital to a center for children suffering from tuberculosis - discharging its last patient in the early 1970s. It has lain fallow ever since, falling into disrepair.

Undercliff is the site of a major confrontation between Cade Williams and the Adversary and is first mentioned on page 233 of *Judgment Day*.

––––––

WAREHOUSE 468

A warehouse at the Red Hook Container Facility, #468 is the location where the Necromancer meets Cade Williams and the site of the ritual intended to bring the Adversary back into this plane of existence.

It is first mentioned on page 194 of *Infernal Games*.

WILLOW GROVE

Willow Grove, Connecticut is the town where Cade Williams makes his home at the start of the Templar Chronicles. (He lives at 841 Didymus Lane, to be exact.) It is first mentioned on page 22 of *A Scream of Angels*.

WORK CAMP 352

Work Camp 352 is a prison work camp set up by the Lord Regent. It is attacked by a group of Templars led by Gabrielle Williams on page 239 of *Darkness Reigns*.

THE WINDING STAIR

The Winding Stair is a long staircase that leads from the streets of the City of Bones down to the docks at the base of the cliffs below. It is first mentioned in the Templar Chronicles on page 214 of *A Tear in the Sky*.

ARTIFACTS

From mystical artifacts to religious relics full of divine power, the world of the Templar Chronicles has its fair share of interesting doodads and whatnots. Several of them play an important part in the story of Cade Williams and the men of the Echo Team

ARCHANGEL'S FEATHER

The feather from an archangel is a potent artifact, as Cade Williams discovers in the Templar Chronicles. At the end of *A Scream of Angels*, Cade is given a tar-black angel's feather and told that he will have need of it in the days to come (page 236). Later, in *A Tear in the Sky*, when he and his companions are lost on the Sea of Lamentations as the result of a powerful storm sent by the Adversary, Cade uses the feather to guide them through the tempest.

EYE OF HORUS

The Eye of Horus appears for the first time in the story "Pig Roast." Cade Williams and the men of the Echo Team are tasked to recover it from a gang of bikers known as the Devil's Swine and they enlist the help of the Night Marshall, Joe Hark, to do so.

Little else is said about the Eye, beyond the fact that it is a dangerous artifact that the Templars cannot allow to fall into the wrong hands.

––––––

THE HAND of St. Bernard of Clairvaux

The Hand of St. Bernard is a holy relic that first appears in the Templar Chronicles on page 104 of *Infernal Games*.

Church legend claims that the hand is that of Saint Bernard of Clairvaux, a former French abbot who founded the Cisterian Order and was involved in the Second Crusade. Bernard died in 1153 and was originally buried at Clairvaux Abbey.

His body was exhumed in 1792 in order for his remains to be moved and reinterred at Troyes Cathedral. It was during the exhumation that it was discovered that Bernard's right arm was perfectly preserved, as if he had been laid to rest an hour before rather than six hundred some-odd years earlier. The soldiers sent to transport the body amputated the limb at the elbow and in time legends of miraculous healings became associated with the relic, prompting the Pope to order a full investigation.

At some point in the mid-eighteenth century the Church sent the artifact to the Abbey of St. Lucius, where it was stored in a ornate gold and glass enclosure in the Chapel of the Sacred Hand until Cade steals it for the Necromancer during the events detailed in *Infernal Games*.

––––––

Hand of Glory

A Hand of Glory is a mystical artifact created from the severed left hand of a murderer hung on the gallows for his or her crimes. The resulting mummified hand is a potent piece of black magick and can be used for a variety of nefarious purposes, including but not limited to locating a missing person or object, putting an enemy into unnatural sleep, forcing a confession, and opening any lock or door.

In the Templar Chronicles, the Hand of Glory is first mentioned on page 80 of *A Tear in the Sky*, when Cade Williams finds one in the possession of Father Joseph Martin, a Catholic priest from the Church of the Blessed Sorrow, who has apparently used it to open a permanent portal into the Beyond for reasons unknown.

———

Necklace of Yum Cimil

Yum Cimil is the Mayan god of death. He is often represented in the Mayan culture as a skeletal being adorned in the bones of his victims or as a body covered with the black spots of decomposition. As ruler of the nine-level underworld known as Mitnal, Yum Cimil is judge, jury, and executioner when it comes to the souls of the dead and it is believed that he takes great delight in torturing those who deserve punishment. According to legend, those who have committed particularly grievous crimes have their eyes torn from their sockets and added to a necklace that Yum Cimil wears about his neck, granting him access to the power inherent in their evil souls.

The necklace of Yum Cimil is first mentioned in the Templar Chronicles in the short story, "Down Where the Darkness Dwells," which tells how Simon Logan became the leader of the Council of Nine. The story originally appeared in the anthology

Urban Enemies published by Gallery and is reprinted in this volume.

Soul Blade

Also known as Gabriel's Tears, the soul blades are seven blades of power "forged in the heart of an angel's sorrow" from the remains of the sacred sword given to him by the hand of the Almighty.

According to the archangel Uriel, three of the blades have been lost to history. Two are controlled by the demon Abromolech, hidden deep in his warrens beneath the city of Moscow and one rests in the hands of the enigmatic Preacher. The final soul blade is given to Cade Williams (page 213 of *Judgment Day*), so that he can use it to strike down the Adversary and send him back to the Infernal Realm.

The blade given to Cade is described as a dagger with a simple, unadorned hilt and an fragile-looking uneven blade.

The Spear of Destiny

The Spear of Destiny is the Roman lance used by the centurion Longinus to pierce the side of Christ while he hung on the cross. It is first mentioned in the Templar Chronicles on page 125 of *The Heretic*.

Also known as the Holy Lance or the Lance of Longinus, the Spear has long been rumored to have certain mystical properties, including the legend that whoever possessed the weapon would be invincible in battle and would ultimately be able to conquer the world. Napoleon attempted to obtain the Lance after the Battle of Austerlitz, but it had been smuggled out of the city prior to the start of the fight, and he never got hold of it. Charlemagne carried the Spear through forty-seven successful battles, but died when he accidentally dropped it. Barbarossa met the same fate only a few minutes after it slipped out of his hands while he was crossing a stream.

The modern history of the Spear isn't as well documented, according to Templar records. Somehow it eventually wound up in the possession of the House of the Hapsburg and was placed in the Hofberg Treasure House in 1912, where Hitler was later to "discover" it. A rabid student of the occult and fully aware of the legend attached to it, Hitler had the Spear moved to St. Catherine's Church in Berlin shortly after he came to power. As the Americans and Russians advanced on Berlin, he had it moved again, this time to an underground bunker to protect it from Allied bombing raids. That bunker fell to the U.S. on April 30, 1945, and an Army officer took possession of the weapon. Consistent with the legend, Hitler committed suicide in his bunker just eighty hours after he lost control of the Spear. General Patton was particularly interested in the weapon and took the time to have its authenticity traced. His fanaticism on the subject was eventually brought to Eisenhower's attention, however, who found the whole subject distasteful. It was Eisenhower who returned the Lance to its rightful location, the Hofberg Treasure House where the Templars would later take possession of it, replacing it with a replica that would pass all but an arcane inspection.

Another legend claims that the true Spear was stored in the Church of the Holy Sepulchre in Jerusalem until it fell into the hands of the Turks upon the sack of the city. Sultan Bayezid II supposedly sent it to Pope Innocent VIII with a request to keep his brother and rival a prisoner in Europe. It remained in the Vatican treasure vaults until Benedict XIV had it encased in the pilaster dedicated to Saint Longinus in St. Peter's Basilica in the mid-18th century. After coming into possession of the actual relic, the Templars chose to allow this legend to persist, knowing it would help prevent potential relic hunters from learning the truth.

In the Templar Chronicles, the Spear appears in *The Heretic*, where it is stolen by Simon Logan, the Necromancer, from the reliquary beneath the Bristol Commandery as part of the Adversary's plan to bring down the barrier between the living world and the Infernal Plane. Cade's defeat of the Necromancer returned the weapon to Templar custody, where it remained until he clandestinely smuggled it out of the reliquary for use in his battle against the Adversary in *Judgment Day*.

———

Spirit Chains

Spirit chains are manacles created from the "bodies" of captive souls in the Beyond. When they are placed on an individual, they slowly drain that individual's energy and willpower, rendering them unable to summon the will to resist and escape. The touch of spirit chains feels icy cold to the living and prolonged use can result in death as the ghosts leech the life force from their captive.

Knight Lieutenant Sean Duncan is bound in spirit chains before he is taken aboard the Black Rose by Bishop on page 185 of *A Tear in the Sky*.

———

THE STAFF of Anubis

Anubis is the jackal-headed Egyptian god of the afterlife. He carries a long wooden staff, also known as a was-scepter, with a forked base and a stylized animal head at the top that symbolizes his dominion over the underworld.

The staff has long been recognized as a powerful weapon for controlling the dead and the Templars were quite relieved to take possession of it after the battle of El Alamein.

It is mentioned for the first time in *Infernal Games* on page 156 when Cade Williams is instructed to steal it from the Reliquary by the Necromancer.

––––––

The Staff of Moses

According to the Book of Exodus, the staff was a walking stick possessed by Moses that was used to bring water from a rock, helped part the Red Sea, and was transformed into a snake and back again, among other miraculous events.

The staff was passed from generation to generation until it disappeared at the time of the destruction of the First Temple, only to be rediscovered by the Templars in the tunnels beneath the Temple Mount in the early days of the Order. It has remained in their possession ever since. (The artifact that is on display in the Topkapi Palace Museum in Turkey is a fake.)

The Staff is first mentioned in the Templar Chronicles on page 124 of *The Heretic*.

––––––

Veronica's Veil

According to legend, Veronica encountered Jesus on the Via Dolorosa while on his way to Calvary and paused to wipe his face with a cloth she carried with her. In doing so, the image of Christ's face was imprinted on the cloth via supernatural means and the relic became known for its mystical abilities to heal with a touch.

The Templars have possessed the relic since the early sixteen hundreds and it is one of the artifacts that Cade sees in the Reliquary when he visits it for the first time on page 124 of *The Heretic*.

EQUIPMENT

Without the equipment designed and produced by the Templar Directorates of Weapons & Supply and Science & Technology, the average knight wouldn't stand a chance against the supernatural beasts and magickal entities that they come up against on a daily basis. Here are some of the weapons and gadgetry that keep the Templars alive to fight another day...

BLESSED SWORDS

Every Templar knight is given a sword blessed by the Holy Father during their investiture ceremony. The blades are made from the finest hardened steel the Templars can produce and then imbued with magick to make them more effective against the supernatural forces the Templars face regularly.

Every sword is also inscribed with the Latin word *Defensor*, meaning defender. Against Templar rules, Cade Williams's sword is inscribed with another word on its reverse side; *Ulcisor*, meaning vengeance.

_____

BONE MICROPHONES

Bone microphones, or bone mics for short, are communication devices that use bone conduction to transmit sound directly to the cochlea of the wearer. They are a standard part of the Templar strike teams communication rigs and are first mentioned on page 1 of *The Heretic* during the Echo Team's assault of Juan Alvarez's hideout.

_____

BREACHING **Rams**

Breaching rams are specialized tools used by law enforcement and military personnel to force open closed or locked doors. Most are rectangular bars of high-grade steel with handles that allow them to swung forward against a barrier with significant kinetic energy.

Echo Team uses a pair of breaching rams to enter Juan Alvarez's safe house on page 1 of *The Heretic.*

_____

CERAMIC BODY ARMOR

Over their flame-retardant jumpsuits, Templar strike teams wear ceramic body armor designed to protect them from the weapons - natural, supernatural, or man-made - of their enemies.

The Templar body armor is first mentioned on page 209 of *The Heretic.*

_____

CODE BLACK

Code Black is an emergency protocol set up by Knight Commander Williams to protect elements of the Order in the wake of an all-out catastrophic attack. Knowledge of the protocol was limited to the senior commanders of the six elite strike teams and their executive officers.

Upon receipt of the signal - a text simply stating BLACK - the team commanders were to immediately scatter to the four winds, taking their units with them if possible. Caches of weapons, ammunition, and other supplies were secreted at various locations and each team was assigned a different cache to collect and bring to the rendezvous point, an abandoned quarry north of Fairfield, Connecticut on the edge of Hilltop National Park.

The signal for Code Black is issued by Captain Riley on page 210 of *Fall of Night*.

———

COMBAT KNIVES

Combat knives are part of the standard set of equipment carried by all Templar strike units. They are wide-bladed knives primarily designed for hand-to-hand fighting and close quarters combat.

Combat knives are mentioned for the first time in the Templar Chronicles on page 100 of *The Heretic*.

———

FLAME-RETARDANT JUMPSUITS

When going into combat, all Templar units wear flame retardant jumpsuits of grey cloth. The jumpsuits are devoid of insignia or identifying marks that might indicate where they were created or to what unit the men and women wearing them might belong.

These standard issue jumpsuits are first mentioned on page 209 of *The Heretic*.

————

Flashbangs

Also known as stun grenades, flashbangs are nonlethal explosive devices that emit a loud sound and a bright flash of light designed to disorient an enemy's senses. Flashbangs are often used by law enforcement and military personnel to render potential enemies harmless. They are tossed them into a room or building where individuals are suspected to be lying in wait.

Flashbangs are first mentioned in the Templar Chronicles when the Echo Team uses them in their surprise assault of Juan Alvarez's safe house on page 2 of *The Heretic*.

————

Flash suppressors

First mentioned on page 209 of *The Heretic*, flash suppressors are devices that are attached to the barrel of a rifle to reduce the visible signature of the weapon when it is fired by dispersing the burning gases that exit the muzzle.

————

Heckler Koch MP5

In the first edition of the Templar Chronicles novels, the Heckler Koch MP5 submachine gun is the standard weapon of the Templar knight strike teams.

First produced in the 1960s by a team of German engineers

from Heckler & Koch GmbH, this weapon now has more than 100 variants and is popular among police and paramilitary units the world over. It uses a 15, 30, or 40 round detachable box magazine and fires at a rate of 800 rounds per minute.

HECKLER KOCH MARK 23

The Heckler & Koch Mark 23 is a semi-automatic pistol chambered in .45 ACP and is the standard handgun of the Templar Order. It often comes with a laser targeting device and a suppressor.

The HK Mark 23 is first mentioned on page 109 of *The Heretic*.

INFRARED BEACONS

Infrared beacons are small, defensive devices about the size of a hand grenade that, when activated, emit a signal invisible to normal sight but "bright as hell" in the infrared spectrum. IR beacons are often used by Templar strike teams to confuse creatures that use the infrared spectrum for sight.

IR beacons are first mentioned during the battle with the ghouls on page 67 of *Tooth and Claw*.

M107 BARRET "LIGHT" 50 caliber rifle

The M107 Barret "Light" 50 caliber rifle is a shoulder-fired semi-automatic sniper rifle produced by Barret Firearms Manufacturing. It is the preferred weapon of Knight Sergeant Nick

Malone despite the fact that the Templars issue the M24 US Army sniper rifle to their anti-personnel teams.

The Barret is first mentioned on page 210 of *The Heretic*.

———

M24 US ARMY sniper rifle

The M24 US Army sniper rifle is a bolt-action rifle with a five round internal magazine calibered in 7.62x51mm ammunition that is built by Remington Arms. There is a civilian model available as well.

Praised for its accuracy and dependability, the M24 is the standard issue sniper rifle for the Templar strike teams and is first mentioned on page 215 of *Judgment Day*.

———

MK17 SCAR-H automatic rifle

In the second edition of the Templar Chronicles novels, the Templars' standard weapon, the HK MP5, has been replaced by the MK 17 SCAR-H automatic rifle, giving the Templars more contemporary weaponry than the first edition stories.

The MK 17 SCAR H (H for heavy) is a 7.62mm x 51mm carbine assault/sniper rifle currently in use by various special forces units the world over, including the Templars. The weapon comes with three different interchangeable barrels that allow it to be used as a close quarters combat weapon, an assault rifle, and a sniper rifle, depending upon which barrel is currently in use. Its four Picatinny rails allow the mounting of a variety of military standard compatible accessories, including the MK 14 grenade launcher.

The MK 17 SCAR-H is first mentioned on page 3 of *The Heretic*.

―――――

MOSSBERG 590AI tactical shotgun

The Mossberg 590AI tactical shotgun is a 12 gauge pump shotgun manufactured by O.F. Mossberg & Sons. It features a 20-inch barrel, built-in shotshell storage, and often comes with a Pickatinny rail for accessories.

The Mossberg 590AI tactical shotgun is the favorite weapon on Master Sergeant Matthew Riley in the Templar Chronicles and is first mentioned on page 210 of *The Heretic*.

―――――

MOBILE COMMAND CENTER

Mobile command centers are large, fire-hardened vehicles designed to be used for communications and command functions. The one used by Cade Williams in *A Scream of Angels* (page 57) was built on a Freightliner chassis and came equipped with a 450hp diesel engine. It had workstations for eight and seating for eleven. In a pinch, the conference room could hold fifteen, though quarters would be tight. Interior electronics were powered by a 20-kilowatt generator and included satellite TV receivers, video surveillance cameras mounted externally on a thirty-foot telescoping mast, UHF and VHF radios, mobile data computers, and other related communications and surveillance equipment, all of which were secured against intrusion. The center was also equipped with a twelve-foot glide room.

―――――

NIGHT VISION GOGGLES

Night vision googles use image enhancement technology to collect all available light, even in the infrared spectrum, and amplify it to allow the wearer to see in near total darkness. Night vision devices are standard issue for Templar shock teams and are first mentioned on page 209 of *The Heretic*.

N.O.M.A.D.

The Near-autonomous Observation and Mobile Armament Delivery system, or N.O.M.A.D. for short, is a military robotic vehicle used by the Templars. Built on a rectangular base, it is small enough to maneuver through confined spaces of less than a meter in width and can make a neutral turn in just under a meter and a half. Its reinforced treads allow it to manage trenches, curbs, or stairs with equal efficiency and its meter-high rotating turret provides the perfect platform for both two-way audio and multiple optical systems. The vehicle's top speed is just over five kilometers per hour.

The vehicle can be controlled through a cable, fiber optics, or radio system, with a range of up to 1,000 meters. It comes complete with a fully-articulated robot arm that can be extended six meters in length and rotated a full 360 degrees. The arm ends in two robot claws for grasping and lifting objects weighing up to 150 kilograms. Seven weapon mounts are scattered about the chassis to hold a diverse payload of armaments.

N.O.M.A.D. is used by the Echo Team when they begin their investigation of the Eden Facility in *A Scream of Angels* and appears for the first time on page 60 of that volume.

Tactical helmets

Another piece of the standard Templar kit, all strike team members wear helmets made of lightweight Kevlar designed to provide protection in combat situations. Such helmets are padded and shaped for ergonomic fit and also provide mounting points for a wide variety of devices, from night vision goggles to communications equipment. They are first mentioned on page 210 of *The Heretic*.

———

TEMPLAR CHALLENGE

According to the Rule, a Templar must give an enemy an opportunity to surrender before violence is invoked by calling out a ritual challenge. (One reason Cade Williams finds the Rule to be hopelessly antiquated!) The challenge was developed centuries ago and has remained the same, to wit: "In the name of the Lord Almighty, I call upon you to relinquish your weapons and receive the mercy of Christ the King."

Knight Lieutenant Sean Duncan calls forth the challenge when faced with a group of sorcerers from the Council of Nine on page 145 of *The Heretic*.

———

TEMPLAR HISTORIES

The Templar Histories are large tomes stored in the Archives Secretum Vaticaun that record the history of the Templar Order. They are first mentioned on page 164 of *Darkness Reigns*.

———

Templar motto

The original motto developed for the Order is still the one in use today - Non nobis, Domine, non nobis, sed Nomini tuo da glorious; Latin for Not to us, Lord, not to us, but to your name be the glory.

The motto is first mentioned on page 137 of *Darkness Reigns*.

V22 Osprey

The V22 Osprey is a vertical takeoff and landing aircraft used by the Knights of the Red Fist and first appear on page 235 of *Darkness Reigns*.

Zip Ties

Also known as cable ties, zips, and wire ties, zip ties are a type of fastener made from hardened plastic that is used to hold items together. Originally designed to organize electric cables or wires, they are now used for a wide variety of purposes, including as makeshift handcuffs by law enforcement and military personnel.

Zip ties are standard equipment for Templar assault squad personnel and are first mentioned in the Templar Chronicles on page 92 of *The Heretic*.

MAGICK

There is power in the universe, power that can be harnessed and used for a variety of ends if one knows how to go about doing so. The act for calling forth and controlling that power is known as magick in the world of the Templar Chronicles. From illusion to necromancy, modern sorcerers bend the world to their own ends, sometimes intentionally and sometimes not.

Here are some of the common magickal processes and items that appear in the Templar Chronicles

Cade's Gift

Cade Williams has the ability to "step beyond" into the world of the dead, a realm of existence just beyond our own, by passing through any reflective surface. The damage he sustained to his right eye has also given him the ability to see into this realm at any time.

Cade's Gift is first mentioned on page 77 of *The Heretic*.

———

Cade's sight

What Cade Williams calls his "sight" is in fact the psychic phenomena known as psychometry, the ability to read recent psychic impressions or emotions left on objects through the touch of his hands. Because of this, Cade wears gloves at all times to protect him from unwanted readings, for the physical and emotional sensations can be dangerously overwhelming.

Cade's Sight is first mentioned on page 26 of *The Heretic*.

—————

Cryogenic spell

The name is a bit of a misnomer, for a cryogenic spell does not "freeze" its target but instead places the target in a kind of suspended animation, essentially slowing all body functions, including infection or disease, for the duration of the spell.

Such a spell is used on Cade Williams after he is poisoned by Dante's Tears on page 222 of *Darkness Reigns*.

—————

Dante's Tears

Dante's Tears is a poison created by combining the blood from several different types of demons and then weaponizing the result through ritual magick. Cade Williams is the only individual known to survive a dose of Dante's Tears; until that point it had been 100% fatal to anyone who came in contact with it.

Dante's Tears are first mentioned on page 220 of *Darkness Reigns*.

—————

Hellgates

Hellgates are portals that lead directly to the Infernal Realm rather than the Beyond. They are first mentioned in the Templar Chronicles on page 40 of *Darkness Reigns* and again on page 166.

Illusion spell

An illusion spell is a type of magick designed to hide the true nature of a person or object. Cade Williams used such a spell to cover the back door out of the complex in the abandoned quarry.

This type of magick is first mentioned on page 61 of *Darkness Reigns*.

Minor and major wards

Designed to guard a specific location or object, wards are one of the mainstays of modern magick. They come in two types; minor and major. Minor wards are just what the name infers; minor magicks that can be used to protect an object or a location for the short term. These can be performed by a single individual with limited preparation, often on the fly. Major wards are another story entirely, intended to last indefinitely and requiring several days of preparation by a sorcerer with considerable power, using several acolytes to assist. They are not undertaken lightly and the slightest mistake can have disastrous consequences. Major wards that fail outright often end in the deaths of all involved in the casting.

Wards can also be used to keep someone or something confined to a particular location.

Cade Williams hires Denise Clearwater to erect wards

around his wife Gabrielle's body after he recovers it from her grave in *A Tear in the Sky* (page 26).

———

Nero's Torches

Nero's Torches are light sources used in Lesser York made from setting captive humans alight with magical fire and letting them burn within iron cages for illumination.

Such devices are first mentioned on page 180 of *Darkness Reigns*.

———

Obfuscation Pendant

The obfuscation pendant is a necklace given to Gabrielle Williams by Knight Major Thomas Hale. The pendant was enchanted with an illusion spell designed to hide Gabrielle's true identity and to make her appear as a human male to anyone who looks upon her. (Curiously, the pendant did not work on Cade Williams, perhaps because of the angelic blood running through his veins.)

The pendant is first mentioned on page 171 of *Darkness Reigns*.

———

Scrying

Scrying is the act of using magick to locate a person or object. Templar mystics use a scrying ritual to attempt to locate the Necromancer on page 32 of *Infernal Games*.

———

Walking the Mirror's Road

Walking the Mirror's Road is the nickname Cade Williams has given his ability to use the reflective surface of objects, especially mirrors, to enter into and return from the Beyond.

This term is first used on page 156 of *Infernal Games*.

PART II: SHORT FICTION

AUTHORS NOTE

Along with the eight novels and four novellas produced in the Templar Chronicles series to date, there have also been a number of short stories set in the world of Cade Williams and the Adversary. Here are three tales that fill in some of the behind-the-scenes details mentioned in the series.

DOWN WHERE THE DARKNESS DWELLS

(**Author's Note:** "Down Where the Darkness Dwells" was originally written for the anthology, Urban Enemies, which featured stories written from the perspectives of the villains from a variety of popular urban fantasy series.

This particular tale describes the events that made Simon Logan, aka the Necromancer, the leader of the Council of Nine and takes places a few years before the events of *The Heretic*.)

The cave gaped like an open mouth and staring at it, Simon Logan had no difficulty understanding why the local tribesmen regarded it with superstitious dread, thinking it an entry to Hell itself.

Then again, he, like the others with him, knew all too well that some superstitions were routed in truth and that this was likely one of them. It might not be Hell they were descending into to, but all their research suggested it just might be close enough.

"Well? What are you waiting for?"

Logan took a moment to arrange his features into an approximation of pleasantness before turning to face the speaker.

Jonathan Hale was a tall, hook-nosed blond with an air of superiority only matched by his power over the dead. He led the necromantic Council of Nine with ruthless efficiency. The mages in his inner circle were powerful sorcerers in their own right, though none matched Hale's ability, and one day Simon hoped to join their ranks. For now, however, he had to be content with serving as an acolyte, learning at the knee of men like Hale until his own, meager powers grew into something more tangible.

It was a necessity, but Logan didn't have to like it.

The team was here in the jungles of Honduras hunting for an artifact of considerable power known as the Necklace of Yum Cimil. They'd landed four days earlier at Toncontin International Airport, where they were met by the guide Hale had hired to take them into the interior. They'd loaded their gear into a pair of off-road vehicles and driven for hours before camping the first night at a small village outside of Azacualpa. Then, at dawn the next day, they made their way on foot into the jungle. Three days of hiking through difficult and dangerous terrain led them to this cave hidden in a thicket of mangrove trees.

It was Logan's job to lead them inside. Not because he had any particular experience in spelunking; no, that would be too logical for a man like Hale. Instead, Logan had been selected to lead the group for the simple reason that he was the most expendable. Cave fodder, so to speak. If anything were to go wrong, Logan would be the first to tangle with it, potentially giving the others time to safely retreat from the problem.

And he wonders why I'm reluctant to get underway, Logan thought. Still, he'd agreed to accompany the team so there was nothing to be done about it now but shoulder on.

He spoke a word of power and watched as the end of the torch he carried burst into green flame. The arcane fire would burn brighter than normal flames, but wouldn't give off the heat or smoke that were the byproducts of a traditional torch.

More relevant, in Logan's eyes at least, was the fact that it would burn endlessly until it was extinguished by the mage who had created.

We might be going down into the underworld, but we won't be doing so in the dark, at least.

A final glance back to be certain they others were ready and then, with an impatient nod from Hale, Logan stepped forward and passed through the mouth of the cave.

———

The tunnel sloped downward at a deceptively gentle angle, but it went on for a long way, and by the time it leveled out Logan had no doubt that they were a couple of hundred feet below the surface. The tunnel was high enough for him to walk upright without fear of banging his head and wide enough that they could have walked two abreast if Hale had ordered them to, which he did not. It was cool and dry, unlike the jungle outside, and the rock underfoot was mostly free of rubble, which made movement easy.

Logan could almost imagine he was out for a bit of afternoon exploring if it wasn't for the sense of oppressiveness that hung over the place and the knowledge of what they'd come here for.

Yum Cimil was the Mayan god of death. He – *it?* - was often represented in the Mayan culture as a skeletal being adorned in the bones of his victims or as a body covered with the black spots of decomposition. Ruler of the nine level underworld known as Mitnal, Yum Cimil was judge, jury, and executioner when it came to the souls of the dead, believed to take great delight in torturing those who deserved punishment. According to legend, those who had committed particularly grievous crimes would have their eyes torn from their sockets and added to a necklace that Yum Cimil wore about his neck, granting him access to the power inherent in their evil souls.

Logan and the rest of the expedition team were here because Hale believed that the necklace was stored in a chamber deep within this cave system and he intended to retrieve it for his own. Doing so wouldn't be without its challenges; there were more than a few stories about those who ventured into the cave system being lost in the darkness forever and Logan was enough of a realist to believe that there was some truth to those stories.

He was no innocent, after all. He'd stopped being one of those the day he'd discovered his talent for necromancy. That had radically changed his life and he was determined to cultivate his power in any way possible. If that meant raiding the tomb of an ancient Mayan death god, so be it.

They had been moving through the tunnel for nearly twenty minutes when a rough chamber opened up ahead of them. It was rectangular in shape and clearly man-made; tool marks could be seen on the walls and the floor was covered with some kind of crude stone tile.

Word went back through the line and a few moments later Hale stepped up beside Logan.

"Do you see the path?" Hale asked.

Logan shook his head. There was a thick sheen of dust on the floor, covering most of the tiles, and it didn't look like anyone had come this way in a very long time.

Hale gave voice to several words of power and then flung the energy his spell conjured up into the room before them. It ripped through the small space blowing the dust from the surface of the stones and turning several of them as dark as charcoal before the power exhausted itself against the far wall.

In its wake, a clear path across the room was laid out in darkened stones.

"Stay to the path; do not stray from the revealed stones," Hale told him.

Logan wanted to ask what would happen if he miss-stepped, visions of poisoned dart traps ala Indian Jones running through his head, but the look on Hale's face told him in no uncertain tones that he really didn't want to know. Apparently ignorance truly was bliss.

Logan set off, carefully making his way across the room step by step, never straying from the darkened stones. Then, and one by one, the others followed until they were all on the far side.

With their first obstacle successfully navigated, the group continued onward.

They moved as quietly as possible, as if afraid of waking something lingering here in the depths of the earth. No one spoke and the only sound was the occasional rock rolling away underfoot or the swish of their equipment brushing up against the tunnel walls.

They had just moved through a long stretch of straight tunnel, the sameness of the rock around them lulling them into a kind of mental daze, when Logan stopped short, causing the next man in line to bump into him, nearly sending them both to their deaths.

Less than five feet in front of Logan the floor abruptly ended even as the curved walls went onward, creating the illusion that the tunnel continued ahead of them.

If he'd been looking forward rather than down at his feet...

He shook himself, chasing away thoughts of what could have happened, even as the man behind him passed the word back down the line to hold in place.

Logan took another step forward and stood with his torch extended, looking over the edge of the drop.

At the bottom of the cliff face, forty, maybe fifty feet below, the tunnel continued forward on the opposite side of the chamber.

While this particular trap hadn't been included in their intelligence brief, they'd come prepared for a wide variety of eventualities.

"Ropes!" Logan called and two of the men behind him got to work, removing long doubled-nylon climbing ropes from their packs and securing them to the tunnel floor with pitons brought along for just that purpose. When they were ready, the ropes were passed up the chain to Logan, who threw them over the edge. The other ends of the two ropes cascaded down the cliff face to lie in a puddled heap at the bottom.

Length was not going to be a problem, it seemed.

Logan fashioned a makeshift harness by straddling the rope, wrapping it around his hip and then over his left shoulder, around his neck, and back down past his right arm. The weight of his body would act as a brake as he slowly lowered himself down the side of the cliff.

Bones crunched beneath his feet when he reached the bottom; the remains of jungle animals who had wandered into the cave mouth in search of food and had apparently not paid enough attention to the path ahead. Logan glanced at them fondly for a moment – he was at home with dead things – and then unwrapped the rope from his body and shouted for the others to make their way down.

When Hale and the rest of the group had made it down to his level, Logan took the lead once more. The first two obstacles had been successfully navigated, but there were certainly more to come and Logan found himself growing increasingly nervous as his sense of security was slowly stripped away. At some point, one of these traps was going to get them; he was sure of it.

About fifteen minutes later Logan brought the group to a halt once more. This time, he found himself staring at a narrow rock bridge that stretched across a gaping chasm in the tunnel that dropped away for hundreds of feet below them.

The bridge looked to be about a fifty feet across, maybe a bit more, but what it had in length, it lacked in width. Logan figured it was no more than six inches across and that was here at the start, where it was the widest. The center of the span looked to be just inches in width and would require putting one foot very carefully in front of the other if one were to hope to cross.

Logan turned and called back through the ranks to Hale.

"We should probably rope ourselves together-"

He didn't get any further.

"And have you drag me to my death when you slip and fall? Not a chance, you imbecile! Get moving!"

Fucker, Logan thought, but he got moving nonetheless, not wanting those behind him to crowd him on the narrow causeway ahead.

Taking a deep breath, he put his arms out to either side to help his balance and stepped out on the bridge.

It felt sturdy enough beneath his feet, which would help. He didn't want to think about what crossing this thing would be like otherwise. Setting one foot carefully in front of the other, he began making his way across.

He was fine for the first few steps; psychologically he knew he could always turn and through himself back to the ledge behind him if something were to go wrong. But as he got farther out, the realization that there was nothing to hold on to, nothing that could support him in the event of an emergency save the narrow walkway beneath his feet, began to take its toll. His body began to tremble as if with cold, the shaking impacted his balance, and suddenly Logan found himself with his body wobbling side to side as he tried to take another step. His foot skittered off the rock in front of him and for a frantic moment he thought it was all over - he was going to slip off the stone bridge and plummet hundreds of feet to his death in the darkness below – but then his foot found purchase and he managed to steady himself anew.

Easy, he thought to himself, as his heart raced like wildfire and he tried to regain control of fear. *You can do this. Another twenty feet, that's all.*

Summoning his courage, he managed to get himself moving again and before he knew it he'd reached the other side. He stepped off the bridge onto the far ledge with a huge sigh of relief.

He turned, gave the hold sign to the next man waiting in line, and then pulled a rope of his own out of his pack. He attached a cam to the rope with the help of a nylon sling, then seated the cam deep in a crack in the nearby wall. He used a second cam to anchor the rope even more firmly in the same manner and then tugged on the rope to make sure it would hold. When he was satisfied, he stepped up to the edge of the bridge and hurled the other end of the rope back across the gap to his companions.

A man on the other side secured it in a similar fashion and suddenly they had a hand line to use as the rest of them made their way across. Even Hale made use of it, though he couldn't be bothered to compliment Logan on his foresight and ingenuity when he reached him on the other side.

When the team was safely across, Logan took point once more. The tunnel began to twist and turn at sharp angles, growing narrower as well, and Logan was suddenly thankful that he didn't suffer from claustrophobia.

He had just finished squeezing himself through a particularly narrow section when the passage ahead of him opened up and he found himself on the threshold of another chamber.

Holding the torch in his hand high above his head, Logan took a good look around.

This room was rectangular in shape and about twice the size of the previous chamber, but still small enough for the torch in Logan's hand to reveal the interior to him. On the far side of the room, stood an altar. Atop the altar was a stand made from human bones and hanging on that stand was a necklace.

That was what they had come for; the Necklace of Yum Cimil.

It barely drew a glance from Logan. He was far more interested in the room's other occupants.

They stood between him and the altar, lining both sides of the room, two ranks of dead Mayan warriors in full regalia on either side of the room. The weapons and feathered headdresses they wore looked as fresh as the day they had been placed there but their bodies were dry and desiccated with mummification.

Logan had seen his share of dead bodies – what necromancer hadn't – but something about these particular corpses left him feeling unusually unsettled. Before he could figure out why, however, the rest of the party caught up with him and he had no choice but to step into the chamber to allow them room to do the same.

"At last!" Hale exclaimed, pushing past Logan to stride between the silent guardians on his way to the altar.

Logan felt something shift in the air around them.

He glanced about, taking in his fellow acolytes as they examined the stalwart warriors and Hale as he climbed the steps of the altar to examine the necklace atop it, but he didn't see anything that set his internal alarms to ringing.

And yet...

Something had changed. He was certain of it.

Unable to figure out what that something was, however, Logan turned his attention to the mummified warrior standing in front of him. He stepped closer, peering into the dead man's face, wondering who he had been and what had possessed him to give up his life to stand here in this chamber for the rest of eternity.

Had he done so voluntarily? If so, what had prompted such a sacrifice?

Motion from the direction of the altar caught Logan's attention and he turned that way just in time to see Hale lift the necklace free of its bone stand and carefully place it in the silk-lined wooden box being held by one of the other acolytes. Hale spent the entire time berating the other man, telling him to hold the box steadier, to lift it higher, to stop staring at the artifact with such greed; a litany of failures that was one of Hale's hallmark responses to those he considered inferior. Logan couldn't wait for the day when he was powerful enough to best the man...

When Logan turned back, he found the dead warrior's eyes had opened; the corpse was staring directly at him. Or would have been, had there been eyes left in the dead man's sockets.

Logan froze, staring back, wondering if the man was actually staring at him or if the dead man's eye lids had flicked open as a result of the disturbances they were generating in the air of the chamber after all this time.

When the warrior turned his head to follow Hale as he strode past Logan on his way to the exit, there was no longer any doubt.

"Look out!" Logan cried, even as the warriors surrounding them sprang to life and attacked.

Two of their numbers lost their lives in those first few second as the Mayan warriors lashed out with their spears, impaling both men through their chests before they even knew what was happening. Logan used the torch in his hand to parry the strike of the dead man in front of him and then swung it like a club, crushing the other's skull.

Logan's exultant cry of victory died stillborn in his throat, however, as the warrior picked himself back up and came at him again, the spear in his hand just as dangerous as before.

In seconds, the room was utter chaos. Acolytes were fighting for their lives against the undead guardians of the necklace while at the same doing their best to protect their leader. Hale, meanwhile, was preparing to cast a spell of banishment; Logan recognized the hand motions even as he did his best to keep the creature in front of him from skewering him like a piece of meat.

A horrified scream burst from the man next to Logan as one of the other warriors managed to get past his guard and sink his teeth deep in the flesh of the man's arm. Logan looked on in horror as the life was literally sucked from the other man, his flesh shriveling right before Logan's eyes as the Mayan warrior drank his fill. In seconds the acolyte was reduced to little more than a shriveled husk, much like the Mayan before him.

Now that he understood the consequences of letting the Mayan get his hands on him, Logan redoubled his efforts to keep the other at bay, mentally screaming at Hale to hurry it the fuck up!

Logan didn't know if Hale heard him – *who really knew the extent of the man's powers?* – but in the next second a powerful wave of magick burst from the Council leader's fingertips, washing across the room like a miniature tsunami, sweeping over everything in its path. Logan could feel the tug of the magick as it swept over him, but it was looking for the dead, not the living, and so it didn't have any effect on him.

As for the Mayan warriors, that as another story.

The spell had been cast by a master necromancer, with all of his power behind it. Rather than attempting to control the creature, it was designed to rip the life force animating them from their dead flesh and cast it aside, leaving nothing more than inanimate husks in its wake.

One minute Logan was feverishly fighting for his life, the

next the Mayan warrior in front of him collapsed to the floor like a puppet that had just had its strings snipped.

Turning, Logan found the same was true for all of the other warriors; the room was littered with their desiccated corpses.

"Quickly now," Hale said, clutching the box containing the necklace tight to his side as he stepped over the shriveled body in front of him and headed for the door.

Logan didn't need a second invitation to follow suit.

He was almost at the entryway when the sound of something dragging itself across the floor behind him drew his attention.

He spun around to find the dead men that were littering the floor stirring back to life, the force that had animated them visibly rushing back into their bodies like smoke sucked into their mouths.

Logan couldn't believe what he was seeing. For the dead men to resist a banishment spell cast by a master necromancer of Hale's ability was so utterly outside Logan's experience that it was the equivalent of waking up to find the inmates had taken control of the asylum. He stared in horror as the corpses began to move with a bit more alacrity, dragging their limbs behind them even as they sought to follow those who had dared to disturb their sleep and steal the precious artifact they had been placed there to protect.

"Run!" Logan shouted, then took his own advice.

The next several moments were a blur, as the group of artifact seekers fought their way through the narrow twists and turns of the tunnel leading back to the bridge. As they hurried along, Logan was aware of the sounds of pursuit growing behind them and he knew it wouldn't be long before the warriors caught up with them. He wanted to move faster, but was hampered by those ahead given the confines of the tunnel, just as the man behind him was hampered by Logan's progress.

Things came to a head when they reached the bridge as the

man behind Logan tried to shove his way past, sending them both sprawling. Logan managed to catch himself against the tunnel wall, but the other man wasn't so lucky; his scream seemed to go on a long time as he slipped over the edge of the bridge and plummeted into the darkness below.

The man's death barely gave Logan any pause; he had a horde of undead Mayan warriors at his heels that would be just as happy to throw him off the bridge as his companion had been and he wasted no time in scrambling back to his feet and headed out onto the bridge. Never in his life had he been so thankful for his foresight in stringing the guide line, for he would never have been able to make his way across the stony bridge without it.

The fall had cost him precious time, though, and the horde at his back had gained on him as he reached the opposite side. He glanced back, saw the dead men rush onto the bridge without slowly, and knew his lead was dwindling by the second. With his heart in his throat, he rushed after Hale and the others.

He'd barely gone another twenty yards before one of the Mayans tackled him from behind. The pair crashed to the floor, the dead man losing his grip on the necromancer in the process. Logan didn't let the small blessing go to waste; he scrambled to his feet, snatched the torch he'd dropped off the floor, and ran headlong down the tunnel even as the dead man behind him was crushed beneath the feet of the rest of the undead rushing forward.

When Logan reached the point where they had descended the cliff face to reach the lower tunnel, he found those above rapidly pulling the ropes up behind them.

"Hey!" he shouted. "You can't leave me here! Throw me the rope!"

A glance back down the tunnel showed the horde closing in on him.

"Hey!"

There was no reply from above; they continued working in silence, ignoring his pleas.

Fuck!

Logan looked frantically about, searching for another way up. He spotted what looked like what might be a grabbed the rock face in front of him, tried to leverage himself up with his bare strength, but there were too few handholds and he slid back down in seconds.

He turned, put his back to the wall, and watched the pack of mummified warriors getting closer with every step. If he didn't get out of here, he was a dead man!

The dead Mayans were less than twenty feet away when he spotted it; a small hole in the wall at floor level to his left. He hurried over and bent down to check it out; it was a tunnel, leading heaven's knew where, but wide enough that he could probably fit in it if he squeezed his shoulders tightly.

He didn't give it another thought, just threw himself into the opening, squirming forward as quickly as he could, reaching up and pulling himself forward with his hands while pushing with his feet.

The Mayans didn't hesitate, either. The lead warrior followed him right into the tunnel; Logan could hear it scrambling along in his wake.

If he didn't do something, the creature was going to grab his feet and it would be all over pretty quickly after that. Even as the thought occurred to him he felt the thing's fingers scramble across the sole of his boot; another few inches and it would have had him.

Logan did the only thing he could think of. He relinquished his hold on the spell illuminating his torch, pointed his hands back down the tunnel behind him, and sent a bolt of power into the ceiling just above his feet.

The walls shook around him as his bolthole was plunged into darkness and Logan prayed to every dark god he could think of that the roof wouldn't come crashing down on his head. He scrambled forward as the ground beneath him bucked and swayed and the tunnel was filled with the rushing roar of falling rock.

And then, silence.

Logan lay still, the neck of his shirt pressed over his mouth, doing his best not to breathe in all the dust filling the narrow tunnel around him. He listened for pursuit, but didn't hear anything beyond the occasional settling of the stone behind him.

Hopefully this tunnel went somewhere and he hadn't just entombed himself beneath hundreds of feet of solid rock. Escaping one horrible death to suffer another wasn't his idea of a good time.

First things first; he needed light again. He felt around ahead of him until he located the torch he'd been carrying, then reached deep inside and tried to call forth a bit more power to light it up

Nothing happened.

Uh oh...

He tried again, but the well had run dry. The bolt of power he'd used to collapse the tunnel had depleted his energy reserves. He wouldn't be able to conjure up a light for some hours now, not until his body had a chance to rest and regenerate his internal energy stores.

Crawling around down here in the dark was not his idea of fun, but at the same time he didn't want to just sit still and wait for his mojo to return. If any of the Mayans had survived the rock fall – and why not, they were already dead, right? – they could be digging through to him at this very moment. He didn't want to be here when they managed to dig themselves out from under.

Best to keep going and look for a way out while he still had the strength to do so.

Inch by inch, foot by foot, Logan began slithering forward as best he was able. The darkness was absolute and he began to feel like it was a living thing, surrounding him, hemming him in, pressed against every inch of his body until he wasn't certain where it ended and he began. He wanted to scream and shout in fear and frustration but was afraid the second he opened his mouth the darkness would swoop down inside him, diving deep into the depths of his very soul, and that would be the end of him.

So he gritted his teeth and clamped his mouth shut and kept crawling, ever forward.

After what seemed like forever, the tunnel slowly grew wider, enough that he could get up on his hands and knees and move forward a bit more expeditiously, but the lack of fresh air combined with his physical exertions soon pushed him into a haze of dizziness despite the extra space. All he wanted to do was lie down in the middle of the tunnel and go to sleep, but something inside told him that if he gave into that urge he might never rise again, so he pushed on, moving forward little by little. He lost track of time and then lost track of the fact that he'd lost track of it, until it felt like all he'd ever done was crawl forward on his hands and knees, feeling for a way out.

When the tunnel floor disappeared from beneath him, it was almost a relief.

He reached forward with his left hand, just as he had a thousand, maybe ten thousand times before, except this time there wasn't anything there to hold him up. His hand went down, down, down farther still and by that time the weight of his body had tipped forward and he fell right out of the end of the tunnel he'd been crawling along and dropped into nothingness.

He let out one short, sharp cry and then slammed into the stone floor twenty-five feet below, knocking himself unconscious in the process.

———

———

———

Logan woke to excruciating pain, his right leg broken in two places. He screamed when his hand accidentally brushed against the shaft of bone sticking out of his shin and promptly passed out again.

Time passed.

When he came to a second – *third?* – time, he found that though his leg was still broken, his pain had settled into a low grade hum in the back of his mind. He wondered, briefly, if he was dying. Had he perhaps lost so much blood that his body no longer had the capacity to feel the pain? If that was the case, then why was he thinking so clearly?

It didn't make sense and so, with no facility to puzzle it out, he just let it go.

He focused instead on the cavern around him, which, he realized with no small shock, he could actually see. A thin shaft of moonlight was shining into the chamber from a hole in the ceiling high above. He glanced upward to its source and then followed it down as it slashed through the darkness to land on the face of a figure seated on the other side of the room. Logan jerked in surprise at the sight and was struck with such an overwhelming sense of danger that he physically raised his hand in front of his face to shield himself.

When several seconds passed and the figure failed to move or speak, he sheepishly lowered his hand and gave the other a longer look.

Whoever he'd been, it was clear he'd been dead a long time. Like the warriors in the hall of the necklace, this man's corpse had shriveled and blackened with age. His lips had pulled back from his teeth in a death's head rictus and his eyes had sunken so deep in his skull that they were all but invisible. He was dressed in the remains of some kind of primitive robe and a necklace of small round stones hung across his chest.

Logan stared at the necklace, a suspicion growing in that back of his mind.

Those aren't stones...

The notion that he'd found the missing eyeballs of the dead Mayan warriors in the hall above wouldn't go away.

His gaze drifted from the necklace to the throne on which the man sat. What he'd first taken as whitish stone revealed itself in the moonlight to be a massive collection of human skulls. Iron bands, looking strangely fresh after what was certainly ages beneath the surface, bound the man's extremities to the throne itself.

He might once have been a king, but he'd ended his life as a prisoner, Logan thought, *trapped down here where the darkness dwells just like I am now.*

He must have drifted off for a bit, for when he came to again he found that he was a bit closer to the throne than he'd been before. Had he crawled forward in his sleep?

The idea was a bit unnerving, he had to admit, but not as unnerving as the sense that the man – thing? – on the throne seemed to have moved since he'd last looked at it. Where before it had appeared to be sitting up and staring straight ahead, now it appeared to be leaning forward, its head cocked a bit to the side so that it could look directly at Logan.

It's a trick of the light, he told himself, but deep in his heart he didn't quite believe that.

Not really.

But like his injuries, his mind didn't really want to dwell on who, or what, he thought the thing on the throne really was.

Logan was looking about in the dim light, searching for another way out beside the hole in the ceiling three stories above, when he heard the voice.

Simon...

It was faint, almost at the edge of his hearing.

At first he thought he'd imagined it, but after a moment he heard it again.

Simon...

"Who's there?" he called out and was shocked at how weak his voice sounded even to his own ears. It was little more than a whisper itself.

I'm here, Simon.

"Hale? Is that you?"

No. That murdering bastard deserted you, Simon, left you to suffer for his own mistake.

The thought sent a spike of red-hot anger pouring through Logan's frame, jolting him a bit into greater awareness.

"That fucking bastard," he mumbled to himself, no longer wondering just who he was talking to, but focused instead on the subject of the conversation.

Yesssss. He must be punished for what he's done to you, stranding you here.

Logan laughed, a high, cackling sort of laugh with more than a touch of madness in it.

"Punished?" he said. "I'm not going to punish him. I'm going to rip his lungs out and kill him."

The voice was silent as Logan went on mumbling for a bit, ranting really, talking about all the ways that he was going to fuck one Jonathan Hale nine different ways from Sunday if he ever made it out of this god-forsaken place...

I can help you with that, you know.

"Help me with what?"

Getting out of this forsaken place. Isn't that what you just said you wanted? To get out of this place so you can make that bastard pay...

Another laugh. "In case you haven't noticed, Yum, my legs pretty messed up. I'm probably bleeding to death right now and I don't even know it. Probably making you and everything else in this place up, figments of my imagination as my brain gets starved for oxygen as my veins pour out on the ground."

I assure you, I am quite real.

For whatever reason, Logan believed him. And he played the only hand he saw before him.

"Okay then, pop my bones back into place, knit my flesh back together, and we'll get out of here. The two of us, together. You help me, I'll help you. Deal?"

There was the sound of a gasp in the darkness, as if the other couldn't quite believe what he'd just heard, and then a quick succession of rapid pops.

Almost like iron clasps being broken under immense force...

Logan had a second to wonder just what he'd done, and then the figure from the throne was bending over him, its bony teeth shining in the darkness, the eyes on the necklace around its throat all turning as one to stare at him in horror.

This won't hurt a bit, the other said, and then a hand clamped itself over one side of his face as a searing heat burned itself deep into his flesh and his head was filled with the triumphant laugher of a being that should have remained locked in its prison deep beneath the earth until time itself passed all meaning now free to wreak havoc where and when it wanted...

The Adverary was prisoner no more.

———

———

Six Months Later.

The door to the mansion in the swamps outside New Orleans crashed inward from a savage blow and then Simon Logan strode into the room, staring with satisfaction at the surprised occupants and disrupting the ritual that they'd just begun.

One of them stepped forward.

"What's the meaning of this?" he cried. "How dare you intrude on-"

The speaker, one of the senior mages of the Council of Nine that Simon Logan had once longed to emulate so badly, never got any further. Logan waved a hand and the man began choking to death, his throat collapsing inward upon itself as if it had been struck by a great weight.

As the man struggled to escape the fate he'd called down upon himself, the other men in the room fell silent, stunned into inaction at the power of the man they thought long dead, the man who had once been nothing more than an eager acolyte but now returned to them as a powerful sorcerer in his own right.

It was just the reaction Logan was hoping for.

He searched their faces, one by one, looking for his target. Not seeing him, he addressed the man nearest to him and asked, "Where's Hale?"

This man was perhaps a bit smarter than his colleague, for

rather than protesting he simply turned and pointed in the ranks of those behind him.

Sensing where this was going, the men standing in that part of the room quickly separated, leaving Logan staring at the man he had come here to kill.

Hale's mistake was in not attacking the moment Logan entered the room. The extra time gave his opponent time to prepare his defenses, so when the attack came, which they both knew it would, it crashed against a wave of arcane force far more powerful than Hale anticipated.

Logan gazed calmly at Hale as the other stood there, bewildering at his one-time apprentice's newly found power.

"My turn," Logan said with a smile.

When he was finished, there wasn't much left of the former necromancer but a few bloody bits of flesh clinging to the walls.

Logan addressed those still standing in the room.

"I hereby claim leadership of the Council of Nine, its power and authority granted to me by the rite of trail by combat. Any objections?"

There were none.

As he turned, intending to seek out his former master's study and see just what artifacts and books of power he had hidden away, the voice of the Adversary spoke into his mind from hundreds of miles distant.

Oh, we are going to have so much fun, you and I.

So much fun.

Simon Logan, now the most powerful necromancer in the United States, merely chuckled in agreement.

PIG ROAST

Written in conjunction with Sam Witt

———

(**Author's Note:** This story was originally written for the anthology, Urban Allies, which featured collaborations between pairs of urban fantasy writers. I had the pleasure of working with Sam Witt and this story stars his character, Joe Hark, aka The Night Marshall, as much as it does Cade Williams and the Echo Team. Sam's Night Marshall novels are terrific and I'd urge you to pick them up and give them a read. They are well worth your time.

———

In the chronology of the Templar Chronicles, Pig Roast takes place after the events of *The Heretic* but before those detailed in *A Scream of Angels*.)

"They called themselves the Devil's Swine, which, if you ask me, is pretty damned appropriate," Knight Commander Cade

Williams said as he tossed a set of surveillance photos down on the conference room table for the other members of the team to examine.

The first several images were classic "look-down" shots mostly likely taken by a drone and showed a stretch of rough-looking men in leather vests and jeans moving down a stretch of highway astride motorcycles. The bikes were a mix of classic Harleys and custom choppers, the club emblem – a tusked boar – prominently displayed on several gas tanks as well as on the backs of the men's vests.

Cade went on. "Intelligence has been tracking these guys for months now, believing them to be responsible for the cross-country transportation and delivery of certain stolen artifacts moving from one group to another. Word is that they've just taken possession of a particular object known as the Eye of Horus and we've been tasked with getting it back."

The next set of images were "on-the-ground" shots, most likely taken by an undercover human operative with a long-distance lens. Surprisingly, they were grainer than the previous set of photos, making it hard to make out individual facial features despite the relative nearness of the subjects to the photographer. When Cade had first seen the photos his initial thought had been that someone should teach the photographer to clean his damn lens, but now he wasn't so certain it was the photographer's fault at all, given what he knew.

Cade's second in command, Master Sergeant Matt Riley, held up one of the photographs.

"What happened here?" he asked, turning the shot so that the other two men at the table, Sergeants Nick Malone and Sean Duncan, could see as well. It was one of the aerial photographs and it showed the line of bikers coming around a bend and entering a thickly forested section of the roadway only to be swallowed up by a thick, black mass covering two-thirds of the image. "Guy get his thumb in the way?"

"Not exactly," Williams replied, tossing a few more photographs onto the table top. All of them showed the same thing – a dark black mass and nothing more.

"Those pictures are why the four of us are sitting here right now," he said, as they looked through the images. "And before you ask, there was nothing wrong with the drone that took them. Tech has taken the camera off the drone and run it through every test imaginable. It works perfectly."

"Jamming, maybe?" Duncan asked.

Malone, the stocky redhead who doubled as the team's sniper in addition to being its electronics expert, shook his head. "If it is, it's a type I've never encountered before." He turned to Cade. "Do we know the extent of the anomaly?"

Using the touch screen keyboard set into the surface of the conference room table, Cade called up a map of Missouri and displayed it via the wide screen monitor hanging on the wall at the far end of the table. A section of the map in the corner of the state was highlighted in red.

"That," Cade said, pointing at the highlighted region, "is Pitchfork County, Missouri. A lovely little backwoods-kind-of-place and home base for our motorcycle happy friends. And, amazingly enough, it also happens to be one of the few place in the whole damned country where our surveillance equipment fails on a regular basis, even when there is nothing wrong with the equipment itself."

The others had been around long enough to pick up on Cade's sarcasm and read between the lines. There was something in Pitchfork County, something unnatural, and it was going to be their job to root it out while they dealt with the bikers and located the Eye.

The four men gathered in the room were members of the

Order of the Poor Knights of Christ and the Temple of Solomon, otherwise known as the Knights Templar. Most of the world thought the Order had been destroyed in 1312 when Pope Clement V, in cooperation with King Philip IV of France, ordered its members forcibly arrested, tortured, and eventually burned at the stake. The two patriarchs had been after the Templars' vast wealth, but the treasury, as well as many of the Order's members, were never found and eventually disappeared into the mists of time and legend.

Cade and the others knew the truth, however. The Order had not disbanded but had instead gone underground, using their wealth to hide themselves away from the world while working to continue their sacred mission; protecting mankind from supernatural threats and enemies. When Hitler and his demonic allies had threatened the world in the 1940s, the Order had emerged from the shadows, reuniting with the organization that had given birth to it in the first place, the Catholic Church, and thrown all of its weight and power into the fight against the powers of darkness. In the wake of the Allies victory, the Order became the de facto combat arm of the Vatican, continuing their mission to this very day.

Williams led the Echo Team, one of six special operations units within the Templar hierarchy and was responsible for dealing with all supernatural activity in the U.S. They were supported by several mainline combat units, but Echo was the best of the best; when everything went straight to hell, they were the guys that got called to make things right.

Which brought them to today's briefing.

"We are to liaise with a guy on the ground by the name of Joe Hark. He knows his way around and we'll no doubt benefit from his knowledge of the locals, but we're to keep things as close to the vest as possible when dealing with him. The Preceptor was very clear. Priority number one is tracking down that biker gang and recovering the Eye before they have time to pass it on to its intended buyer. Priority number two is to make sure that the gang is no longer operational by the time we leave. If, and only if, we manage to accomplish those two objectives are we free to investigate anything that might be contributing to our inability to generate surveillance of Pitchfork County. We clear?"

The other three men nodded; they were veterans, they knew the drill.

On the other hand, they also knew their commander and not a single one of them had any doubt that he was going to do things his way, regardless of what the Preceptor wanted.

Such was life when working with the men the Templars called the Heretic.

———

———

———

Joe cupped his hands around the unopened can of Busch and let the chill soak into his palms. Though it was February, the temperature inside Smokey's House of Meat felt more like high summer than midwinter. The heat intensified the shack's accumulated reek from decades of smoke and spilled beer, but the burnt ends and pork ribs more than made up for that.

Joe hoped the New Englanders he was here to meet would feel the same way.

By the time a black Expedition rolled into the gravel parking lot, the unopened beer had slicked the Night Marshal's hands with a layer of condensation that had warmed to room temperature. Joe didn't wear a watch, but by his reckoning the city boys were more than a little bit late. He'd expected them for lunch and it was well on toward supper time. He stood from the rickety oak table and hollered into the kitchen, "These boys are gonna be hungry, Smokey. Get 'em a couple racks of ribs and whatever burnt ends you can rustle up."

Joe headed out into the cold winter air, drying his hands on the thighs of his jeans as *he went to greet his visit*ors. They're looking for some*one, the Long Man had told Joe. Show them around, keep them from poking their noses where they don't be*long. Try not to start a fight.

That last would be easier said than done. The men piling out of the Expedition looked like they'd seen more than their fair share of trouble and were expecting even more. They weren't displaying any obvious weaponry, which was a good first step, but their uniform gray coveralls didn't even try to hide the bulges and seams of the body armor it covered.

Joe grinned as he approached the team's obvious leader. The man looked worn ragged and pissed, a combination that gave Joe pause. The Night Marshal stopped well back from the newcomers, giving them space. He shoved his thumbs into his front pockets to show them he meant no harm and said, "I reckon we've got two choices. We can tussle out here in the cold until we decide we're both on the same team and ought to work together or you fellas can get out of the cold and enjoy the best barbecue this side of Texas."

The eye-patched man kept right on scowling but inclined his head toward the door. "I don't know about you, but we missed lunch. Let's eat."

———

———

———

Cade didn't know what to make of the man they called the Night Marshal, but he had to agree this barbecue was something special. The five of them ate together in silence, tossing stripped rib bones onto a sheet of butcher paper in the center of the table.

Cade was irritated the trip had taken so long, and he couldn't help but feel the Night Marshal had given them inadequate directions as a way of putting the 'city boys' in their place. They'd driven for hours trying to find the right combination of gravel back roads and potholed state highways to reach their destination, wasting time they couldn't afford to let slip through their fingers. But, as irritated as he'd been when they finally arrived, the barbecue had blunted the edge of Cade's temper. It was hard to stay pissed with a belly full of perfectly smoked pig meat.

He sampled one of the burnt ends, and the glazed chunk of blackened protein buried the last of his anger. It was rich and savory and sweet, like a piece of chewy candy forged from smoke and sugar and meat so tender it almost melted on his tongue. For a moment, all Cade could think about was how much he was going to miss this when he went back to Connecticut.

He needed to satisfy his curiosity, still. He sat back in his chair and stretched. "I had a hell of a time finding this place. If I didn't know better, I'd say someone didn't want us here."

The Night Marshal grinned, and Cade thought the expression would've looked more at home on a shark. "Maybe you don't know better. Pitchfork has a way of keeping outsiders where they belong."

Cade crossed his arms over his chest. "And where's that?"

"You know. Outside."

The Templar didn't want to give credence to the idea that somehow the land itself had conspired against them, but he didn't know how else to explain their trip into Pitchfork County,

Missouri. As soon as they crossed the county line the Expedition's navigation system lost its signal and every chance they had to take a wrong turn, they ended up taking it. A trip that looked like less than an hour on the map had taken them almost three to complete. "I guess it didn't get the job done. We're here now. Were you briefed?"

The Night Marshal nodded. "Bikers, charms or some such bullshit, blah blah blah. Just another day in fuckin' paradise."

"That does about sum it up. Where do you want to start?" Cade was itching to get the case resolved and get the hell out of here. There was something about this part of the country that made him uneasy. The sooner he could get his team back to the Ravensgate Commandery, the better.

"Yeah, there's a few places we can hit up. You can ride with me, and your guys can follow us. Stick close. If you get lost, there's no telling where you'll wind up. I don't feel like spending all day rounding up lost ducklings."

Riley bristled at the Marshal's tone, but Cade checked him with a glance. "They're not going to get lost."

Joe gestured at the empty plates and the mound of bones on the table. "All right, then. Looks like everybody's fueled up, might as well get this party started."

———

———

———

There was something off about Cade, but Joe couldn't put his finger on it. It wasn't just his eye patch, or his scars, or the weirdo serial killer gloves. Joe'd never seen anyone eat ribs with gloves before. It was fucking unnerving. Whatever the weirdness was, it went bone deep. Joe figured he'd be able to get to the bottom of it by giving the Templar a supernatural once over, but that seemed a little rude, so he decided to let it lie. He'd keep the conversation light. "You believe this is Left-Hand Path work?"

The Templar didn't respond at first, just stared out the window at the dense forest of leafless trees they were driving through. Then, "It's supernatural, I'll give you that. Perhaps even demonic. We'll find out soon enough."

Joe thought it over for a sec and then nodded. "Right. I forgot. You're Catholic," he said, as if that explained everything.

Which, in fact, it probably did.

He eased the truck onto a thin dirt trail, pumping his brakes to flash the taillights so the Expedition wouldn't miss the turn. He was impressed by the driver behind him; for someone not familiar with Pitchfork's roads he was doing a good job of keeping up.

The road wound deeper into the forest and climbed up the side of a hill. At the peak, Joe killed the truck's engine and turned to Cade. "We're going to have to hike a little bit, so we don't spook this guy. Just follow my lead, you'll be fine."

Joe grabbed his shotgun from the rack in the truck's back window and climbed out into the cold. The rest of the Templars were waiting at the front of the Expedition. Joe raised his voice to be heard over the winter wind and creaking branches. "The guy we want to talk to is down at the bottom of this hill. We'll walk the rest of the way in so he doesn't hear the cars and get spooked. I don't think we'll have any real trouble, but you might as well gear up. He's less likely to start shooting if we look like we're ready to shoot back."

Joe always thought he was a decent enough woodsman, capable of getting through the brush without raising a ruckus, but the Templar's were damn near ghosts. He had to keep looking back to make sure they were still following him and always found them unnervingly close. Where his hobnailed boots made a trail of clear prints in the shallow snow, the city boys left faint tracks that would be hidden by the wind in a matter of minutes. He was impressed.

At the edge of the woods, Joe raised a hand to bring the Templars to a halt. From their vantage, they could see a rusted-out trailer with a makeshift shed grafted onto its side. He turned back to the Templars and drew them into a huddle so their voices wouldn't carry on the wind. "This guy knows bikers; he'll know where to find who you're hunting. But he used to be a meth cook. His brains are...well, he's not all there. He'll act tough and might get weird. Try not to put a bullet *through his brainpan before we have a chance to talk to h*im."

And don't cut him in half with one of those fucking swords, Joe thought to himself.

They crossed the open space between the forest and the trailer without incident. That made Joe more nervous than if the mad old bastard had come out onto his porch with a shotgun. Hyrum was permanently paranoid, and his lack of reaction to their presence was troubling.

Joe eased the shotgun off his shoulder and cradled it in both hands. He climbed up the short staircase and banged on the door with the shotgun's butt. At least he tried to bang on it — the first impact sent the door swinging inward.

Cade whispered from behind Joe, "Maybe he was expecting company?"

Joe rolled his *eyes. Great. He'd teamed up with* sarcastic ninja from New England.

This was going to be a bad day.

———

———

Cade entered the house after the Night Marshal, with Riley and Duncan on his heels. His men swept to the left and right covering the interior of the cramped trailer. Malone stayed on the porch, eyes peeled for trouble. If he saw any coming, he'd put a bullet to the top of its head before it got within 50 yards.

The Templar didn't know what he'd expected, but this wasn't it. A circle of filth and inch deep covered the center of the room, its surface churned and dotted with flecks of pink and white. The stench was incredible, an earthy assault on his sense of smell. "So this is what it looks like when you don't have indoor plumbing."

The Night Marshal chuckled at that and shook his head. He pointed at the couch with a TV tray in front of it, the moldy remains of a frozen dinner resting on the plastic. "Even out here, folks don't shit where they eat."

Cade wrinkled his nose. "You think your guy pulled out and, what? Wild animals got in here?"

The Night Marshal nudged at the filth with the toe of his hobnailed boot. A filthy acorn cap rolled out in front of his foot. "Yes, on the wild animal part. I'm guessing pigs based on these acorns. No, on my guy pulling out."

The Templar looked around the place. There is a thin layer of dust on every surface and from the looks of the leftover food, no one had been here for at least a week. "So where is he?"

Joe jabbed a finger at a cluster of pink-tinged chunks half-buried in the filth. "You big-city folks would probably want a DNA test, but my gut tells me that my guy is right there. Or at least what's left of him."

Cade rubbed his jaw. "You have to be kidding."

"Nope, that's not a joke. Pretty sure that's Hyram. Fuckin' pigs must've eaten him."

Duncan's stomach groaned in protest at the idea. Cade raised an eyebrow in their guide's direction. "You're telling me our lead was eaten by wild pigs?"

Joe shrugged. "I'm not telling you it's a coincidence. Someone knew you were coming and decided to tie up loose ends. They made it ugly to shut down anyone else who might consider being helpful and forthcoming when I paid 'em a visit."

Cade furrowed his brows. "Any idea where we go from here?"

Joe bared his teeth in a grim smile. "Yeah, but you're not going to like it."

The Templar frowned. "Mind sharing any more details?"

"Sure," Joe sad as he headed for the door. "We're going to go and rustle some pigs."

———

———

———

Half-an-hour later the five men were lying on their bellies along a tree-shrouded ridgeline, peering down into the clearing on the other side where an old, abandoned slaughterhouse stood. After leaving Hyrum's place, Joe told them that he had an idea where the Swine might be operating from and had led them through a maze of backwoods roads only to arrive at a spot in the woods that looked like every other spot to Cade. The Night Marshal apparently knew where he was going, however, for after a fifteen minute walk through the woods humping their gear with them on their backs, they arrived at the base of the ridge upon which they now lingered.

The two-story brick building had certainly seen better days,

Cade noted. The glass had been broken out in most of the windows, graffiti covered plywood having taken its place, at least on the lower floor. One section of bricks was stained black with soot, evidence of an earlier fire that had threatened to take the building down with it before it had been put out.

It wasn't so much the look but rather the feel of the place that set Cade's nerves on edge. It squatted there in the center of the clearing like a malevolent spider waiting to trap its prey, and even the air around it seemed to be tainted by its presence. He had expected a certain amount of emotional residue when Joe had told them they were headed for a slaughterhouse, but this was way off the charts.

There was something else going on here.

The first clue, of course, was the fact that the "abandoned" slaughterhouse was no longer abandoned. Several members of the Devil's Swine were hanging around in front of the place. Some were working on their bikes, while others sat around drinking beer and horsing about. All of them were armed in some manner or another; Cade could see an assortment of pistols, rifles, and shotguns being carried or lying within reach of their owners. Two men, both armed with M-16s, stood about half-a-dozen yards away from the others, lackadaisically guarding the entrance to the only road that led into or out of the clearing.

The second was revealed when Cade triggered his Sight; that mystical ability he'd gained when the fallen angel known as the Adversary had tried to kill him, the very event that had prompted his entrance into the Order. His Sight let him see past the Veil and into the Beyond, the Purgatory-like plane between the lands of the living and those of the dead, and seeing the slaughterhouse through its lens revealed the dark heart of corruption that lurked somewhere within its depths. A grey-green miasma rolled off the place in waves, leaking from every opening like a thick fog that was pushing its way out from the inside, and Cade shuddered to think just how much black arts it had taken to taint the place so heavily.

If this wasn't the source of the electric "jamming" that was interfering with their surveillance, it was at least a contributing factor. If the Eye was anywhere in Pitchfork County, Cade suspected this would be the place.

A burst of movement among those in front of the building caught his attention and he turned to see a long, white Cadillac coming down the access road. The guards moved out of the way and let the vehicle pass without stopping it and, given the way the bikers practically leaped to attention as the car pulled up in front of the slaughterhouse, Cade figured they were about to meet the Swine's head honcho.

Turned out he was right.

One of the bikers opened the rear door of the Cadillac and a painfully thin-looking man in a dark suit unfolded himself from the back seat. He was dressed in a dark suit that hung loosely on his thin frame and stood several inches above the bikers around him; Cade put his height at 6"4' or so, give or take an inch. The man was fish-belly pale and wore dark glasses, his bald head gleaming in the mid-afternoon sunlight.

The newcomer barked a few orders to the men around him and then headed straight for the entrance to the slaughterhouse.

Just before entering the building, however, the man paused, then turned and slowly looked up toward the ridgeline where Cade and the others were concealed.

For just an instant Cade felt as if a thousand insects were scurrying up his spine and into his brain, but then the feeling *passed and the new*comer stepped through the doorway and disappeared into the depths of the building.

Had they been seen? Cade wondered.

They were under good cover and no one had even done *so*

much as flinch when that guy looked in their direction, but that creepy-crawly feeling nagged at him.

Only one way to find out.

He signaled to the others and they moved back down the slope, where they could talk without risk of being seen or overheard.

"Who's the guy in the Caddy?" Cade asked, expecting Joe to have at least a passing familiarity with the dude, but the other man just shook his head.

"Never seen him before," he said and from his tone it was clear that he wasn't any happier about his lack of information than the Templars.

"Anything we should know about the place before busting in?"

Rather than a quick reply, the Night Marshal gave the question some serious consideration before answering, something Cade respected. This guy knew his business, it seemed.

"This place was built just after the Civil War, so there's no telling what shape the interior is in. Watch where you put your feet; there are bound *to be open d*rains and troughs all over the place in there and you might not see them clearly in the shadows."

Sound advice, Cade thought with a nod.

"All right, here's the plan."

———

———

———

Riley was a mere ten yards from the guards on the road and still they hadn't noticed him. He and Duncan were walking down the access road in plain view, but the guards were facing in entirely the wrong direction — back toward *the slaughterhouse* — and chatting *loudly amongst themselves, which served to cover Riley's approaching* footsteps.

Damned poor security, he thought. If I'd wanted to gun them down I could have done it ten times already.

But he wasn't here to do that, at least not yet. His Mossberg combat shotgun, his preferred firearm for close-in dirty work, was strapped to his back, easily reachable but currently out of sight of the men in front of him. He'd use it when the time came, but for now his mission was to delay rather than destroy.

He stopped walking and heard Duncan's footsteps come to a halt behind him a step later. Hoping the idiots in front of him wouldn't shoot them out of sheer surprise, he said a silent prayer heavenward and did what he'd come here to do.

"Ah, excuse me?" he called out tentatively.

The men jumped as if they'd been goosed with an electric cattle prod and spun around, the guns in their hands coming up in ragged surprise.

Riley held up both hands, palms out.

"Easy there, gents. Easy. Just need a little help, that's all."

To his relief the guards lowered their weapons *toward the ground, apparently* thinking Riley wasn't any kind of threat despite all the visual cues staring them in the face.

Thank God for blind arrogance, he thought.

"Get the fuck out of here," one of them said, waving the tip of his weapon to indicate that they should go back out the way they had come in.

Riley had no intention of doing that.

"Come on, now. Help a brother out, huh? My buddy and I were doing a little deer huntin' and our truck broke down a mile or so back. Just need to borrow a phone to call for a tow and I'll be out of your hair."

"Are you deaf or just dumb?" the other guard asked, scowling. "Turn around and get the hell out of here before we shoot your dumb ass!"

The one on the right raised his gun again and Riley decided he'd given Cade and Joe time enough. He flicked his finger in the prearranged signal and was rewarded a split second later by the sight of the man's head exploding into pieces as a fifty caliber bullet from Malone's Barrett sniper rifle moving at 2700 plus feet per second tore through it with only the barest bit of resistance. The sound of the shot finally reached his ears but Riley was already in motion at that point, crouching down as he ripped his shotgun off his back, bringing it to bear on guard #2 *while he was s*till staring in horror at the decapitated body of his partner who was only just now beginning to topple over.

Like fish in a barrel, Riley thought as he pulled the trigger and cut the other man down as quickly as the first.

––––––––

––––––––

Cade and Joe had moved past the stockyards and were crouched next to a plywood-covered window on the far side of the building when the sound of Malone's shot rang out. Seconds later the air was filled with the sounds of gunfire as Riley and Duncan followed suit and the caught-with-their-pants down bikers tried to respond.

It was the signal they'd been waiting for. Joe stood up, drew back a foot, and slammed it into the plywood, sending it bouncing away into the darkness beyond. He turned and gestured with a smile.

"After you, good sir."

Cade grunted in reply and slipped over the threshold, entering the old slaughterhouse with Joe at his heels.

The smell caught him first, a thick stench of death and decay that hung over everything like a wet blanket, and he had to force himself to keep from gagging. It wasn't just the scent of old death, either; this was fresh and close by somewhere. Whatever these guys were doing, it couldn't be good.

He gave himself a moment to let his eyes adjust and then, after a tap on the shoulder from the Night Marshal indicating he was ready to go, Cade led the way into the darkness.

They moved through room after room like a team that had worked together for years rather than two men who had just met. One of them would kick open a door, *spinning to the left while* the other went right, their weapons up and ready, but space after space met them with empty and open silence.

Where the hell is this guy? Cade wondered.

———

———

———

The bikers considered themselves to be badasses and maybe against the average Joe they actually were, but against the highly trained special operators of the Templar Echo Team, they were woefully unprepared and outclassed.

Riley first shot took down guard #2 and the man's corpse hadn't even hit the dirt before both he and Duncan were sprinting forward, firing at the bikers in front of the slaughter-house as they came.

Normally crossing 200 feet without cover while being fired upon would have gotten them quickly killed, but they had a couple of things going for them; training, surprise, and the fact that Malone was currently causing chaos in the bikers' ranks as he took down one combatant after another from the protection of the ridgeline above.

By the time Riley and Duncan reached the protection of the Cadillac, the fight was all but over.

Things weren't going so well inside, however.

———

———

———

They found the leader of the gang in the next room they entered. Joe kicked open the door and Cade hustled in, the pistol in his hands searching for a target in the shadows, and then a set of floodlights came on with a loud click, bathing the room in their harsh brilliance.

What he saw in their light brought Cade up short.

He was in a wide room with a dirt floor, facing a stage-like platform on which the Swine's leader currently stood, dressed in a robe stained nearly black with accumulated blood and wearing what Cade thought was a pig mask. Surrounding him on three sides were a dozen or more, well, demon-swine was the best reference Cade could come up with to describe them at the moment; large, misshapen creatures that looked like a cross between a human, a pig, and a demon or *two, all pig snouts*, dark beady eyes and thick slabs of calloused flesh.

"Fuck me," Cade heard Joe whisper at his back and he found he couldn't agree more.

Fuck me was right.

Apparently the Swine's leader had seen them on the ridge.

Joe decided taking the offensive was the best move for he stepped forward to stand beside Cade.

"We've come for the Eye, priest," Joe said. "Surrender it now and you'll be dealt with leniently. Make us take it from you and...well..."

The pig-faced leader laughed in his face. "No, Night Marshal, the time for blind acquiescence has passed. I have no intention of surrendering my property, to you or anyone else. I rule here, not you. He told me you were coming, told me the Templar scum would be with you."

Without pause, the man turned and addressed Cade directly. "Tell me Templar, *how's that wife of yours?*"

Joe said something in reply, but Cade didn't hear it. He was staring at the man on the stage in surprise, stunned by what he'd said.

How's that wife of yours?

Cade's wife, Gabrielle, had perished at the hands of a supernatural entity known as the Adversary several years before. It was the same creature that had attacked Cade and started him on the long path that eventually brought him to the Templars and put him in command of the Echo Team. He had been hunting the creature ever since. The fact that the pig-faced man in front of him knew anything about Gabrielle suggested that *the two, he and the A*dversary, were league with each other in some fashion.

Staring at the man, trying to make sense of it all, Cade suddenly realized something.

That's not a mask...

Cade didn't know who, or what, the man before them actually was, but there was no do*ubt in his mind that he* was working for the other side and that condemned him in Cade's mind as surely as if the Adversary was standing there on the platform beside him.

Enough screwing around, Cade thought. Without further hesitation he swung the weapon in his hand up toward its target.

Joe knew there was trouble the minute the porcine-priest revealed himself. This wasn't just some biker gang moving stolen artifacts as he'd been told. This was Left-Hand Path work, no doubt about it, and this guy was giving off vibes that said he had some serious mumbo-jumbo at his disposal.

Normally Joe was the type to crack some teeth first and ask question later, but with the city boy beside him he thought it might be prudent to try to negotiate first. He'd barely started when he caught movement out of the corner of his eye and realized with a start that things were about to go from bad to worse.

Cade's first shot would have taken the priest right between the eyes if it hadn't been for the pig-demon standing beside him. The thing must have caught sight of Cade's gun coming up for it flung itself forward just as the Templar pulled the trigger.

Dark blood and bits of brain matter splattered the face of the priest as the left side of the creature's head intercepted the path of the bullet, deflecting it from its intended target and sending the demon back to whatever hell it belonged in.

The body was still twitching when the priest pointed a finger at Joe and his companion and screamed, "Kill them!"

As one, the other pig-demons charged.

Joe's shotgun roared in response, taking down several of the vile creatures with a single shot while beside him he heard Cade's pistol blasting away. There were a lot of the damned pig creatures, but unlike other things he'd faced in the past at least these things could be killed with the application of a little well-targeted violence, and he intended to deliver quite a bit of that.

Within seconds the room was filled with the acrid scent of gunpowder, the stench of blood and feces, and the grunts and screams of dying pig-demons. When the creatures got too close for the men to use their firearms, they switched to melee weapons, Joe smashing skulls with the stock of his shotgun while Cade laid waste about him with the long sword he'd pulled out of the sheath on his back.

"He's getting away!" Cade shouted over the din an*d Joe glanced over the head of* the pig-demon in front of him to see that the priest had torn open a door at the back of the platform and was in the process of disappearing through it.

Oh, no, you don't you bastard, Joe thought, and redoubled his efforts, forcing his way forward with a few final swings of his shotgun stock until there were simply no more demons left in front of him to fight.

"This way!" he shouted and rushed for the platform, slamming through the door the pig-headed priest had used and stumbling into a dusty, fly-specked office. He growled in frustration as the man dashed through another door on the far side of the room.

Sensing Williams at his heels, Joe charged through that door as well and into a narrow stairwell. A mélange of foul scents flowed up to meet them.

Cade grunted behind Joe. "Blood."

Joe sniffed, then added, "And pig shit."

The Night Marshal thundered down the steps, not even trying to be sneaky. If they didn't catch the priest before he rallied his supernatural defenses, they were fucked.

Crystals embedded in the stairwell's earthen walls shed

pulses of asynchronous orange light, revealing flashes of the priest's back as he took the stairs two at a time.

Joe's hobnailed boots skidded at the bottom of the steps, slipping in a reeking froth of blood and mud and shit, frustrating his pursuit. He could see the priest's filthy-stained robes as the man fled down an earthen tunnel, but the man was gaining ground.

They passed arched openings as they hauled ass down the tunnel after the priest. Joe glimpsed piles of bloody bones and rotting meat and tried not to look at the sigils that flared to life atop the mounds of carrion. The priest was up to something, and they were running out of time to catch him.

Joe put on a desperate burst of speed and his fingertips brushed the priest's robes as they exited the tunnel into an enormous cavern. Then the priest was gone, hurling himself from a muddy ledge. Joe and Cade skidded to a stop at the edge and saw their quarry splashing through the slop at the bottom of a shallow, muddy pit. Shadow forms rippled through the slop around him, forming a protective phalanx of unseen threats.

Joe rubbed his jaw. "Flip you for it? Heads you jump down into the shit and kill him. Tails, I stay up here and watch."

Cade grimaced. "I should've brought a rifle."

A chorus of enraged squeals demanded their attention. They turned to see a growing mob of monstrosities charging down the tunnel toward them. They had the heavy-jowled heads and pointed pink ears of swine, but their faces and bodies were mockeries of the human form. Rows of slick pink nipples ran down their torsos and their hands and feet were sharp, black hooves.

Cade hefted his sword. "Locals aren't very friendly, are they?"

Joe's face split into a shark's grin, and he raised his shotgun. "You just gotta get to know 'em."

Then the pig-demons were on them, screaming and gnashing their teeth as they closed in for the kill.

———

———

———

Cade met the lead pig-demon with a cross-body slash that opened it from shoulder to hip, emptying its innards onto the bloody floor. The creature's death squeals sent its brothers into a frenzy and Cade suddenly found himself surrounded by shrieking demons.

He hacked a hooved arm off one of his attackers, then pivoted to rip the tip of his long sword through the leg of another. He parried a hoof aimed at his head and counterattacked with a pommel strike that split the creature's muzzle to the bone.

Another attacker slipped through Cade's defenses and slammed its hooves into his back. The blow sent the Templar stumbling into another one of the pigs, which snapped yellowed tusks at his face. Before Cade could respond, there was a thunderous roar and he was covered with a thick coating of sticky gore.

The Night Marshal flashed a grin over the gushing stump of the demon swine's tattered neck before turning to blast a smoking crater in another monster's chest. Cade couldn't be sure, but it looked like Joe was enjoying this a little bit too much.

As before, the monstrosities were clumsy fighters but they made up for their lack of finesse with numbers and raw strength. Cade's arms grew weary from the constant hacking and parrying. He'd lost count of how many of the things had fallen under his sword, but the numbers of those still standing never seemed to dwindle.

He tore the head from another of the beasts and once again

found himself eye-to-eye with the Night Marshal. "Can't keep this up, they're wearing us down."

The Night Marshal responded by smashing in the face of a pig-demon with an elbow and slamming a fresh set of shells into his shotgun. "What's wrong, city boy? Arm getting tired?"

Cade growled and plunged his long sword into the heart of another demon. The mob had pushed him and the Night Marshal almost back to the ledge. He glanced over his shoulders and ignited his supernatural Sight. The priest stood atop a pile of offal and bones, head thrown back, arms raised. Thrumming arcs of power surged up from the bloody floor to form a massive shape.

Cade grabbed the Night Marshal's shoulder and shouted, "We've got trouble."

Joe fired his shotgun into the oncoming horde, then glanced at Cade and asked, "What the—"

A shockwave of arcane energy blasted across the ledge and into the tunnel, tumbling the charging demons onto their backs. Cade had to brace himself with his sword to keep from falling over and saw the Night Marshal hunkering forward to do the same.

Cade turned toward the pit and felt his heart sink.

An enormous sow, easily twenty feet high at the shoulder, crouched in the center of the pit, smoking blood running down her snout and off her back. With a shrieking roar, she lowered her head and charged, murderous rage curling her lips back from enormous jagged teeth.

Cade raised his sword but knew that thing would run them down long before they could do enough damage to stop it. He and the Night Marshal were as good as dead.

———

Joe knew they were fucked. The pig-demons were regrouping after the shockwave knocked them on their asses and they'd be back in the fight in seconds. The hell sow would reach the ledge before that, and he had no doubt she'd tear the damned wall down to get at him and the Templar.

He grabbed Cade by the shoulder and pointed at the charging giant. "Jump!"

Joe didn't wait to see if the Templar followed his advice. If they stayed put, they'd be crushed between the charging pig-demons and the sow behemoth. Their only hope of survival lay in getting off that ledge.

Joe's leap carried him over the giant sow's lowered head and onto her bristled back. His boots slid on the creature's bloody flesh and he crashed to his knees. His left hand grabbed a knot of wiry hairs that just saved him from sliding off the thing's back and under its trampling hooves.

Cade landed next to Joe and drove his long sword into the devil-sow's flesh to arrest his leap. Six inches of steel disappeared into the gargantuan pig's meaty shoulder. That got its attention.

The monster threw itself into the muddy ledge, crushing a handful of its demon-pig minions while attempting to dislodge its enemies. It squealed in hellish rage and shook itself with such force that Joe nearly lost his grip.

"That'll be enough of that shit," the Night Marshal snarled. He rammed the gaping barrels of his shotgun between two knobs of the hell-sow's spine and squeezed both triggers.

The shotgun's occult discharge split the air like a peal of

thunder. Silver fire and acidic green smoke gushed from the shotgun and tore a blistered crater in the monster's back.

Its front legs folded underneath it and its blunt snout crashed into the filth-covered floor. It squealed like a piglet on its way to the slaughter, the sound clawing at Joe's ears and hammering at his sanity.

The Templar reared back and drove his blade into the exposed gristle of the demon-pig's spinal cord.

The blade sank home with a meaty thunk.

It should have been a killing blow, even against the creature of the sow's size. Instead, the mortal assault filled the beast with an unholy vigor.

The pig reared back onto its hind legs with such sudden violence that Joe found himself flying through the air, fist still clenched around a clump of bristly hairs.

Fuck, he thought, then slammed into the muck-covered floor.

———

———

———

Cade hung onto his sword, but the weapon ripped free of the monstrosity's spine and he slid off the thing's back and into the blood and shit. He rolled on impact, which was the only thing that saved him from shattering both of his ankles.

He couldn't see the Night Marshal, and prayed his new ally wasn't dead or too wounded to carry on the fight. Cade had to figure out how to kill the damned sow without being crushed beneath the mammoth hooves that smashed down all around him.

He let his supernatural Sight slide into place as he dodged

around a descending hoof. The missed attack splashed him with a foul mixture of gore and manure. Cade retaliated with a wild swing that gouged away a chunk of the beast's leg.

Blood burst from the wound, but so did a coruscating flicker of black light. It was there for the merest flash of a moment, but it showed Cade what he needed to know.

He threw himself away from the trampling devil sow and slid on his chest and belly for a few yards. Then he scrambled forward, sprinting for the spot he'd seen the black light disappear into. He prayed he was right about this.

Because if he was wrong, he'd be dead.

Cade raised his sword and then slammed the blessed weapon into a seething vortex of power.

There was a tremendous flash and a moment of blinding agony, and then Cade was gone.

———

———

———

A hoofed kick slammed into Joe's shoulder, jarring him out of his daze and numbing his arm down to his fingertips. He rolled with the attack and lurched back to his feet, shotgun raised in his good hand.

The Night Marshal squeezed both triggers before realizing he hadn't had a chance to reload. The metallic click against the hollow barrels threw him off balance, and he narrowly avoided the demon's flailing attack. He needed space to reload, but knew he wouldn't get it. He could see more demons plunging off the ledge, hungry for his blood.

Worse, the sow saw him and was headed in his direction.

"Cade!" He shouted. He didn't know where the Templar had gone, but he didn't have time to find out. Joe turned his back on the demons and ran like hell.

———

———

———

Plunging into the Beyond left Cade blind and deaf. Before he could recover his senses, someone stabbed him.

The attack slipped between the armored plates on his right arm and pierced his bicep. Pain and adrenaline shook Cade back to his senses in time to see the priest drawing a wicked blade back for another attack.

With his sword arm useless, Cade lunged forward and hooked the fingers of his left hand around the man's filthy throat. He writhed in pain and tried to gather his power.

The priest was the conduit between this realm and the devil-sow he'd called forth into Pitchfork County. As long as he could draw power from the land of the dead and funnel it into the demon, the thing couldn't be killed.

But the same didn't hold true for the priest. Cade lifted the man up by his throat. "Didn't expect to see me here, did you?"

The priest's eyes bugged from their sockets and his mouth chewed on arcane syllables that couldn't find their way past his lips.

Cade threw the priest to the floor and bore down on his throat with all of his weight.

There was a split-second of resistance, then a wet crunch echoed through the gloom and the priest's eyes went glassy and dark.

As Cade got to his feet the gleam of something metallic caught his eye and he reached down, pushing aside the dead man's robes to reveal the Eye of Horus on a chain around the man's throat. With a quick yank, Cade pulled it free.

Behind him came a churning roar in response. Cade turned and watched as the portal out of the Beyond tied itself into a knot and disappeared.

———

———

———

Joe returned his empty shotgun to its back scabbard and pumped his arms and legs for all he was worth. His lungs burned; running wasn't his normal game plan, but the hell-sow was gaining on him. Something had changed, he could feel the demons' desperation as they closed in on him. The sow paid no heed to the pig-demons she crushed in her pursuit of Joe; their squeals of pain and fear turned the Night Marshal's stomach.

Ahead of him, the lights of the cavern grew dim and a curved wall blocked his path. Joe realized where he was under the slaughterhouse and couldn't help but grin. Maybe he'd get out of this after all.

Joe leaped at the concrete wall and climbed, fingers and toes digging into its irregular surface. Years of erosion from seeping water and more gruesome fluids had left the concrete rough, giving him the hand- and footholds he needed.

"Let's see if you fuckers can swim," he snarled.

———

Pig-headed spirits coalesced out of the grey fog surrounding Cade. He drew his long sword, preparing to wade into the mob before him, then thought better of it.

Live to fight another day was never one of his favorite expressions, but damned if it didn't make sense right about now. He held no illusions about his odds of fighting off that many of the creatures and had no intention of sacrificing himself needlessly either.

Discretion is the better part of valor, a voice in the back of his mind spoke up, one that sounded suspiciously like his dead wife, Gabrielle, and he listened to it, turning to run with every ounce of strength he had left.

All he needed to do was stay ahead of them long enough to find a portal back to the other side.

No pressure.

———

———

———

Joe was thirty feet up the side of the concrete wall when the hellsow plowed into it. The enormous creature didn't even try to slow down, which Joe had counted on. He hugged the wall, knowing that even if this plan worked, there was a good chance he'd end up dead.

The sow's impact sent huge cracks racing up the wall's face, and a massive chunk collapsed into rubble, revealing a pillar of viscous red.

A tsunami of clotted blood gushed from the ruptured silo.

The crimson wave slammed the demonic swine to the floor and washed their bloated bodies into the cavern's walls with bone shattering, blubber-rupturing force.

Even the massive sow was shoved off her feet and hurled against a stone wall. Her legs twisted and gave way with wet cracks as bones split and burst through the skin.

The monstrous swine's wounds oozed thick, black blood and her shattered legs twitched feebly. The Templar must have managed some trick to keep it down. "Thanks, Cade," he said as he stalked toward the fallen pig.

It watched his approach with too human eyes filled with inhuman hatred. Joe pulled his shotgun from its scabbard and cracked it open. He loaded two shells into the barrels and snapped the gun closed.

The sow grunted and tried to lift its head, but Joe pinned its snout his left foot. Despite its size, the thing's strength had fled.

Joe pointed the shotgun at the creature's oversized eye. "See you in hell."

The shotgun's roar echoed through the cavern, drowning out the hell swine's dying scream.

———

———

———

Cade ran as if the demons of hell were at his heels because, well, they were. They didn't move as quickly as he did, their misshapen forms making it difficult for them to get up any decent speed, but he was exhausted from all the fighting and couldn't seem to widen his lead any more than a few dozen yards. As he went, he kept looking around frantically, searching for that telltale gleam of a portal in the distance.

The Beyond was an unusual place and despite all the years he'd been traveling here he had yet to squirrel out many of its secrets. He had learned to control his passage into the Beyond via the Mirror's Road, using any reflective surface to step from the land of the living into this dark and desolate plane of existence, but he hadn't learned how to do the same to get back.

Instead, he was forced to rely on pre-existing portals, gleaming spheres of energy that were mystically tied to some reflecting surface in the real world which allowed *him to travel in the* opposite direction back to the world of the living.

Trouble was, they were few and, sometimes, far between.

And that was in a highly populated area. He'd entered the Beyond literally in the backwoods and the chance of finding a portal in so unpopulated an area was not good.

Not good at all.

But there was no way he was giving up.

A pig-demon got a little too close for comfort and he lashed out with his sword, cleaving off the top of the creature's skull with a single blow, before turning back and concentrating on widening the distance between him and the rest of the pack.

A sudden gleam of light popped into existence about fifty yards to his right and he put on a burst of speed, angling toward it as fast as he could go. The only thing over here that shone like that was a portal, but Cade knew that it could vanish just as abruptly as it had appeared. He had to get to it before it had the chance to do so.

Faster Cade, faster, he urged himself, and bent to the task.

———

———

Joe was standing over the carcass, wondering what the hell he was going to tell the other Templars about Cade, when he felt a faint burst of heat coming from the pocket where he kept his badge.

No sooner had he taken it out than it suddenly flared with heat, causing him to drop it in surprise. He was staring down at the garish red burn it left on the palm of his hand when the badge burst into brilliance, giving off a silver-white light so bright that he had to step back and shield his eyes just to see anything at all.

The light grew, flowing outward, expanding from the center of the badge until it formed a spherical platform a few feet off the ground. It reminded him of a hellgate, the kind of portal that Left-Hand Path sorcerers sometimes used to summon demons to this world, and he stepped back just in case more pig-demons were preparing to come through.

It was a good thing he did, for in the next moment something did, indeed, come flying through the portal.

Not pig-demons as he'd expected, but Cade Williams.

———

———

———

Cade felt that moment of chilling cold that marked the passage from the Beyond back into the real world and then landed with a mucky splash face first in the mud of the pit he'd left behind what felt like hours before.

He heard someone shout his name in surprise and lifted his

head to respond, only to find himself literally face-to-face with the giant demon-sow that he and Joe had been working so hard to kill. The hideous face, so close to his own, made him shout and scramble backward in surprise, which set the Night Marshal to laughing hysterically.

The sheer incongruity of the situation forced a laugh out of Cade, too, and the two men spent a good minute just reveling in the simple fact that they were still alive. Even better, the mission had been accomplished, which was a good thing for all concerned.

When they were done laughing, Joe helped Cade up and the two men filled each other in on what had happened since they separated. They were congratulating each other on a job well done when the rest of the Templar unit burst through a door on the far side of the room, staring at the two men covered in mud and pig shit, wondering what the hell had happened.

Which only set Joe and Cade to laughing all over again.

————

THE MIRROR'S ROAD

———

(**Author's Note:** This story takes place after the events of *Fall of Night* but before those in *Darkness Reigns*. It was written before the latter and at that time I hadn't yet decided that Cade Williams would remain entirely in the Beyond during the fall of civilization and the rise of the demons. As a result, he makes an appearance in this tale in contradiction to later events described in the Chronicles.

When this was written, I was considering a spin-off series told through the perspective of a few people living through the Fall, including the protagonist in this story, Joshua Gideon. Who knows, perhaps I'll write their story at some point, but for now, enjoy this "might have been" moment featuring our favorite Templar hero.)

———

In the moment after midnight, the world held its breath.

Like a finely-tuned watch in need of attention, time slowed, and then stopped. One moment the truck stop was full of noise and activity, in the next everything came to a halt.

In the sudden silence, I looked up from my late night meal of eggs and hash to find the room around me frozen in time. A few tables away, the lithesome teen who moments before had been haranguing her bull-necked boyfriend in righteous anger now stood with her finger pointed at his chest, one hip cocked jauntily as if in unintended invitation. The waitress, a plump matronly woman with too much makeup and a quick, easy smile, had been caught in the act of pouring another cup of coffee for the bearded trucker at the end of the breakfast counter, the liquid suspended in mid-air like a wave on the verge of breaking. The highway patrol officer who'd just hustled in from the parking lot stood halfway between the dining area and the bathroom, one foot suspended inches above the floor.

Even the clock on the wall had stopped, silenced at thirty seconds after twelve.

Everyone, and everything, was still.

Except me.

The sense of déjà vu I experienced in the next moment was almost overwhelming. I'd seen this place before; I knew what was coming next.

And it scared the piss out of me.

Before the thought had fully formed I was up and moving, scrambling away from the weary family in the booth behind me, getting out in the center of the room where my options increased and the chance of collateral damage to those around me would be minimized.

As I moved I kept my attention firmly on the long stretch of mirror that covered the wall behind the breakfast counter. Even as I watched, it grew smoke-dark and frost began to form at its edges.

Too late!

A face swam into view in the glass; long and gaunt, with sunken eyes and hollowed cheeks, a face of winter grey capped by strands of writing hair that twitched and moved with life all their own.

Its empty eyes pinned me with the inerrancy of a laser.

Snarling silently, the chimera pierced the Veil and reached toward me. The mirror's surface rippled, the creature's hand passing through it without resistance, and then the chimera pulled itself into the world, the glass behind it going solid with a sharp snap. Without hesitation the creature leaped across the bar in my direction.

The gun I'd taken off the dead cop in Toledo was out before the beast had cleared the counter, the thunder of the weapon's voice echoing in the confines of the room. My shots struck it full in the face, tossing it backward to the floor like so much discarded garbage, but I knew it wouldn't be down for long.

I'd faced them three times before, but still had no idea how to kill the damn things.

Motion out of the corner of my eye caught my attention and I turned back to the mirror just as several more faces began to form deep inside the darkened glass. I shifted his aim and pulled the trigger. The shot shattered the mirror's surface, closing that exit from the Road.

I knew it would only take the reinforcements a few moments to find another portal. I'd learned the hard way that every single moment counted. Even the tiniest advantage could mean the difference between life and death and I didn't intend to waste a bit of it.

The truck stop's too confining. I'll have a better chance of survival outside, in the open.

I headed for the door, snatching the satchel off the seat next to me on my way.

Things had started going crazy for me five weeks ago, when the woman had appeared in my dreams for the first time. Eyes of green and hair that deep blue-black that seems almost iridescent in certain light. She was standing off in the distance, yelling, but I was unable to understand what she was saying. Each night her image grew steadily clearer, those two almond shapes eyes staring out of a hazy profile that grew more distinct with each passing day, until I could recognize the expression of fear and pain on her otherwise gorgeous face. That night, I'd heard her voice clearly for the first time.

"Run!" she'd cried.

Four of the creatures I now call chimeras had burst through my bathroom mirror moments later. I barely managed to escape in time.

I've been running, and hiding, ever since.

I found the satchel the night before last, in an old abandoned shack several hundred yards off the edge of the highway. I felt drawn to the spot, like the tides pulled by the moon, and when I looked inside the worn leather bag, I understood why. Drawings, dozens of them, had fallen to the floor, quick sketches of scenes that had come and gone: me behind the wheel of a sedan, the sign above the gas station outside of Dallas where the angel had first shown himself to me, the sword-shaped symbol I'd seen burning like a watchfire in the midnight sky a few days later.

She'd seen it all.

I can't tell you how I knew the bag was hers, anymore than I can tell you what keeps me moving inexorably west each night when the sun goes down. I just did and do.

The discovery spurred my interest in finding her. I knew now that she was real. That she was out there, somewhere. I believed that she was trying to reach me in the same way that I was looking for her. Something important, something vital, depended on our coming together and I could no more ignore it than I could stop the sun from rising in the east each morning.

The truck stop was a few hours outside of Oklahoma City, just another of the nameless, faceless establishments that catered to the long-haulers making the run along route 81. The trucker I'd spent the afternoon with was headed north and so we'd parted ways. Not looking forward to a cold night on the road, I decided to grab a bite to eat and see if I could find a warm place to bed down for the night.

Outside the chill October wind immediately wrapped me in its embrace, first caressing softly, and then kicking at the edges of the long coat I wore. Its very motion signaled time's reinstatement; their surprise gone, the creatures had given up on holding the world at bay. They would be coming for me now and damn those who stood in their way.

I had to get out of here!

Several big rigs were parked with their ass-ends closest to the restaurant, their cabs forming a semi-circle facing the ramp back onto the highway a hundred yards away. A solitary streetlight illuminated spaces between the trucks and the entrance ramp. Beyond that was darkness.

I made up my mind without conscious thought, heading for the safety of the darkness, hoping to lose my pursuers amid the washes and gullies of the scrubland I'd seen surrounding the truck stop. Racing between the big rigs, my coat flapping behind me like the wings of some great beast, I tried to stay hidden in the trucks' shadows. If it took just a few extra seconds for the creatures to find me once they emerged from the restaurant, I might have enough time to reach the sanctuary of the darkness and disappear into the night without further confrontation.

Intent as I was watching the door behind me for pursuit, I

didn't notice the hand that suddenly snaked out of the side-view mirror of the rig on my left.

It slashed downward for my face. Some long-buried survival instinct saved my face from being shredded as I ducked away at the last moment, but I didn't duck far enough. The chimera caught hold of my thick head of hair and yanked me off my feet. My gun slipped from my surprised fingers and dropped to the pavement with a clatter.

The pain brought tears to my eyes. I twisted my head, fighting to pull free, as the creature dragged me upward and my feet all but left the ground. In that position, without the counterbalance of solid earth beneath my feet, my efforts were all but useless. Realizing I was getting nowhere, I reached up with both hands instead, turning my attention to trying to pry the creature's fingers out of my hair, but it was incredibly strong; iron would have been easier to bend.

Despite my best efforts, I felt myself being slowly dragged higher off the ground, toward the glass. I cursed my generous head of hair for the first time in my life as I struggled vainly.

Unable to free myself from the creature's grasp, I changed tactics. This time, I kept a hold of the creature's arm with my left, steadied myself, and then swung my right fist at the mirror, aiming for the flat surface above where the chimera's arm emerged. I hoped to shatter the glass and trap the beast between here and wherever-the-hell it came from.

A freakish cold enveloped my clenched fist as it sank into the mirror's depths like a stone tossed carelessly into a pond.

That did it. The terror of my current situation and the events of the last five weeks finally collided. I did the only thing left for me to do.

I panicked.

I kicked and screamed for all I was worth, tearing at the hand that held me. The sound of shattering glass reached my ears, but I was beyond the ability to recognize it. My vision tunneled, my attention drawn to the shimmering surface of the trucker's mirror that was growing closer as I fought and fought and fought...

I felt rather than saw the passage of the sword as it cleaved the space between me and my captor. With a whistling shriek, the finely wrought edge of the blade slashed through the chimera's arm just an inch beyond the point where it emerged from the mirror. I fell heavily to the ground. It took me a second to realize the creature's hand was still tangled in my hair, despite no longer being connected to its arm. Revolted, I pulled it free and tossed it aside.

"Hurry!" he said, kicking my pistol toward me. "Reload your damn gun. We don't have much time!"

The urgency in his voice cut through the haze of fear. I stooped, grabbed the gun, and reloaded with the last of the spare magazines. I glanced over at my mysterious companion as I did. He was tall and well-built, though obviously not dressed for the weather in his jersey and dark jeans. The sword he held was long and thin. A pistol rode in a shoulder holster under his right arm. He stood a half step in front of me and kept his attention fixed firmly on the door of the restaurant, so I was unable to see his face.

"Who are you?" I asked.

I never got an answer, however, for at that moment a shrill set of shrieks and screams came from the interior of the truck stop. Seconds later three more of the beasts spilled through the door and headed for us at a dead run.

I put one of them down with several quickly aimed shots but then the others were too close for me to risk our lives with my poor firearm skills. I needn't have worried. The stranger stepped forth to meet them. In all my life, I've never seen anything like it and doubt I will ever again.

Whoever he was, he knew how to fight. He twisted and whirled like a dervish, never once letting them land a blow as he literally carved them to pieces with that razor-edged sword. Every time the blade met the creature's flesh there was a flash of sharp blue light, like sparks flying from a welding torch, and the faint stench of burning flesh. When he was done with the two he faced, my savior rushed forward and slashed the creature I wounded to pieces before it had a chance to revive.

For the moment, we were alone again.

He turned to me then and for the first time I got a good look at his face. The left side was strong, sharp featured; had I been a woman, I might have called it handsome in a rugged sort of way. The right side, however, was another story. Scar tissue covered it from just above the eye to just below the jaw, looking like a blowtorch had been applied to his flesh, allowing it to melt and reform like the wax of a candle. A black eye patch covered the remains of his other eye and I had no desire to see what lay beneath it.

He caught me staring but didn't seem to care. Instead, he used that moment to dig something out of his pocket and thrust it at me.

"Here. Take this. She's looking for you. It's your job to live long enough to find her."

I took the worn and creased envelope from his hand. It was sealed and looked to have been that way for some time, the once white material faded and yellowed. Written on it, in a fine, spidery hand, was my name; Joshua Gideon. I shoved it into my pocket without opening it.

"Who is she? What does she want? How do I find her?" The questions swarmed like locusts in my mind, tumbling out over one another in my haste to find the answers.

But he had none to give. "I don't know," he said, shaking his head. His voice softened, as if in fond memory. "She walks the mirror's road, like I do. That's all I can tell you."

Alien shrieks came from the inside of the restaurant and his manner turned brusque once more. He turned to face the door, but continued talking over his shoulder to me. "You've got to get out of here. I'll hold them off for as long as I can. Get into the hills and hide until morning. These demons are afraid to walk our world under the light of the sun. You should be safe until then if you find an adequate hiding place."

"But what about you? How will you..."

I got no further. He whirled on me and the anger in his good eye burned white-hot. "Go, you damn fool! While there's still time!"

I did as I was told.

I shoved my now empty pistol deep into the pocket of my coat and charged for the safety of the darkness at the edge of the lot. In just seconds I had left the pavement behind and began the climb uphill, the ground beneath my feet turning coarse and uneven. At the top, I turned to look back.

Below me, in the meager light of that one solitary street-lamp, I could see my mysterious benefactor standing at the ready, sword in hand, facing four more of the creatures. He shouted at them, in what I thought might be Latin, but I was too far away to be sure. As I watched the chimeras charged down the narrow alley made by the parked trucks, heading straight for him. Their bloodthirsty shrieks reached me in the stillness of the night air and I dared not wait any longer, lest they see me.

I started down the opposite side of the hill, warm, wet tears spilling down my face for a man I didn't know, a man who was about to give his life so that I might escape.

One of the creatures must have slipped past his defenses for he cried out in horrible pain moments later, but I didn't turn around.

In the morning, with the rising sun behind me, I wandered back to the truck stop. The restaurant was nothing more than a pile of smoldering ruins, though how the fire started I had no clue. The heat it gave off kept me from investigating further. I wondered what had happened to the patrons who'd been inside when the clock had stopped and then decided I didn't want to know.

The odd smell of cooked meat drifting across the scene seemed to be answer enough.

The bodies of the dead chimeras lay rotting in the morning sun, small wisps of steam rising from the rapidly decaying flesh. I counted seven of them. In another hour, there wouldn't be anything left but a few damp spots on the pavement.

Of my savior, there was no sign.

I felt a moment of hope thinking he might have escaped the onslaught and then glanced again at the burning shell of the building nearby.

Perhaps not.

Removing the envelope he'd given me from my pocket, I carefully opened it. Inside, like the piece of a puzzle I didn't understand, was a postcard.

The color was faded. The edges were frayed. But there was no mistaking the image of the highway sign that adorned its surface, nor the dusty nature of the desert landscape just beyond.

Mystery, New Mexico, the sign read. And in smaller letters at the bottom of the postcard, what I took to be the city's slogan: *Come find your destiny.*

I looked at the destruction around me and then down at the postcard again.

Come find your destiny.

Right.

It seemed my destiny had found me instead.

I slipped the card into my pocket, next to the gun. Pulling my coat tight about me, I turned and walked away from the truck stop, heading up the onramp to the highway above.

New Mexico was a long way off and time was a wastin'.

PART III: THE COMIC

MARKOSIA AND THE TEMPLAR CHRONICLES

Back in 2006 there was a short-lived six issue comic adaptation of *The Heretic* from British comic book publisher, Markosia Comics.

The scripts were written by Chuck Satterlee. Art and coloring was done by Bruce McCorkindale and lettering was handled by Thomas Mauer.

I've never actually held an issue of the series in my hand, but some of the art did make its way to me and I thought I'd share it here. In the next few page you'll find the covers for issues 1-3, as well as an inked and colored page from one issue.

THE TEMPLAR CHRONICLES

H.E.R.E.T.I.C

BASED ON
THE BEST
SELLING
NOVEL BY
JOE NASSISE

1

FEB
2007

SIX ISSUE
SERIES

$3.50 US
$4.30 CAN
£2.00 UK
COVER A

JOE NASSISE
CHUCK SATTERLEE
BRUCE MCCORKINDALE
RICK HILTBRUNNER

MARKOSIA

MATURE
READERS

BASED ON
THE BEST
SELLING
NOVEL BY
JOE NASSISE

THE TEMPLAR CHRONICLES

HERETIC

2

APRIL 2007

SIX ISSUE SERIES

$3.50 US
$4.50 CAN
£2.00 UK
COVER B

JOE NASSISE
CHUCK SATTERLEE
BRUCE MCCORKINDALE
RICK HILTBRUNNER

MARKOSIA

THE TEMPLAR CHRONICLES

H.E.R.E.T.I.C

MATURE
READERS

BASED ON
THE BEST
SELLING
NOVEL BY
JOE NASSISE

3 JUN
2007
SIX ISSUE
SERIES
$3.50 US
$4.50 CAN
£2.00 UK
COVER A

NASSISE • SATTERLEE • McCORKINDALE • SHARMAN • MAUER

McCorkindale/Hoda '07

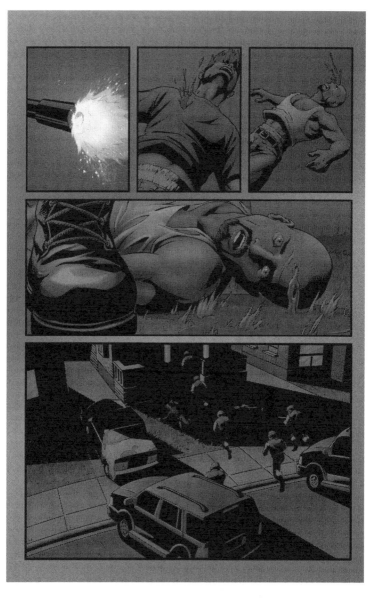

ABOUT THE AUTHOR

 Joseph Nassise is the New York Times and USA Today bestselling author of more than forty novels, including the TEMPLAR CHRONICLES series, the JEREMIAH HUNT trilogy, and the GREAT UNDEAD WAR series.

Joe is a multiple Bram Stoker Award and International Horror Guild Award nominee and served two terms as president of the Horror Writers Association, the world's largest organization of professional horror and dark fantasy writers.

If you want to stay up-to-date on the very latest news, you can follow Joe on Twitter @jnassise, hang out at his Facebook page, or visit his website at josephnassise.com.

For more information
www.josephnassise.com
author@josephnassise.com

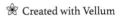

Printed in Poland
by Amazon Fulfillment
Poland Sp. z o.o., Wrocław